14

WITHDRAWN

Makers of Our Modern World

MODERN AMERICANS IN SCIENCE AND TECHNOLOGY

By *EDNA YOST*

Author of *Women of Modern Science*, etc.

Illustrated with photographs

The work of the thirteen native or naturalized American scientists portrayed in this book has in a variety of ways widened the horizons of the twentieth century in which they have labored. Experiments of men like Robert Goddard, Elmer Sperry, Willis Carrier, Leo Baekeland and John Hagen have led to the success of rockets and flights in space, while the explorations of Paul Siple have extended to the last frontier on earth. Enrico Fermi and Vladimir Zworykin have opened new vistas in atomic energy and electronics. George Washington Carver, Frederick Cottrell, Robert Williams and Emil Truog have contributed to man's health, while Charles Kettering has helped to revolutionize his transportation.

The author of several books devoted to scientists, Edna Yost tells the fascinating story of the struggles of these men toward their accomplishments, wherever possible from personal interviews with her subjects. This book, revised in part from an earlier publication by the author, provides an inspiring background for a better understanding of the world in which we live.

MODERN AMERICANS IN SCIENCE AND TECHNOLOGY

Other books by Edna Yost

Puzzle Me This (*with Janet McMaster*)
Modern Americans in Science and Invention
Normal Lives for the Disabled (*with Lillian M. Gilbreth*)
American Women of Science
American Women of Nursing
Modern American Engineers
Partners for Life: Frank and Lillian Gilbreth
Women of Modern Science
Famous American Pioneering Women

"Makers of Our Modern World" Books

MODERN AMERICANS

IN

SCIENCE AND TECHNOLOGY

◆

By EDNA YOST

ILLUSTRATED WITH PHOTOGRAPHS

DODD, MEAD & COMPANY
NEW YORK

Copyright © 1941, 1962 by Edna Yost

Library of Congress Catalog Card Number: 62-20016

Printed in the United States of America
by The Cornwall Press, Inc., Cornwall, N. Y.

For J. Monroe Day

FOREWORD

◆

THE MEN whose sketches appear in this book are modern Americans in the sense that each has lived and worked in the present century. All of them were, or are, American citizens, although four were born outside the United States. All have received high recognition in the fields in which their achievements have been made.

The lives of the group as a whole portray how swift has been man's passage from the Machine Age into the Space Age. They also reveal how dependent scientists and technologists of the Space Age have been upon the work of scientists and technologists who preceded them. Mastery of the use of the gyroscope, as achieved by Elmer Sperry, was essential for success with rockets and space vehicles. John Glenn, Jr., would not have orbited the earth that day in February, 1962, if men like Willis Carrier and Leo Baekeland had not used their talents earlier and well. Air-conditioning systems and plastics are accepted as a matter of course in the many industries which co-operated with scientists in making space flights possible.

Nor will American scientists and space travelers of the future have the personal health and stamina needed for success in their work unless food and soil scientists continue intelligently in the fields pioneered by Robert Williams and Emil Truog. This type of science holds especial significance for young Americans today in view of the fact that comparative tests indicate they are inferior, physically, to young people in some parts of Europe. Unquestionably physical stamina as well as educational stamina has an important place among the foundation stones upon which every nation's youth must build his life achievements. Apparently young Americans need to be using their heads better in learning how to close this gap in physical endurance which is their threatening handicap now.

In planning this book, a variety of fields of science was first determined upon, then an outstanding figure in each field was selected to represent it. Nine of these thirteen chapters have been revised and brought up to date from a previous publication of mine, *Modern Americans in Science and Invention,* which was published in 1941. Reading the biographical sketches in the order in which they are presented shows the essential continuity of science, its links with the past and its arrows pointing to the future. At first sight, it may seem strange to find Paul Siple's name in the list, for geography is often lost sight of as a modern science. Actually, his contributions to the geography of the polar regions, made from the air and by dog-sled trips over terrain hitherto unseen by men, are scientific work linked back to that of our first cartographers and pointing ahead to the geography of the future. It may well be that some who read his sketch here will be among the space travelers who will be the first to map regions still veiled from man's eyes and begin to create pages of the massive atlas which will eventually contain the geography of the planets.

For the author, one of the pleasant aspects of a book of this kind is that it gives opportunity to meet and talk with those who have earned the right to speak with the authority of leaders in their fields. In the work entailed in half a dozen books of biographical sketches, it has been my privilege to talk with and receive friendly co-operation from scores of scientists and technologists of high achievement. One of the impressions that remain with me as a result of these personal contacts is of how deeply these distinguished men and women, native-born and foreign-born alike, cherish the American heritage and want its fundamentals preserved unimpaired.

No one understands better than they that their work has introduced tools into our life which, unwisely used, endanger this heritage. Vladimir Zworykin, for example, recognizes as keenly as any man that television, which he did so much to develop, can be used as easily to dull and befuddle our thinking as to sharpen and clarify it. He knows that freedom of thought, without which the other precious freedoms of our heritage would dwindle, will be dangerously encroached upon unless modern tools, created by scientists, are wisely used to help human beings develop their innate capacity to think. Thinking precedes thought, whose freedom we want to preserve. And only in accepting the imperative need to exercise our capacity for thinking—one of the capacities which distinguishes man from the lower animals—can men fit themselves to form the constant judgments needed for selection and election of proper leaders in a democracy in which our unique American heritage of freedom is at stake.

In my contacts with so many men and women of achievement it has been my privilege to meet some who are great human beings as well as great scientists. To have had this experience is to have had personal touch with greatness. One of the inescapable impressions growing out of the experience is that human greatness is so often—possibly always—accompanied by long hammering against obstacles. Capacity for greatness, no doubt, is inborn. Obstacles cannot create it. But the determination to accept challenges and exert continued personal effort appears to be essential for its development. In my experience, young people of promise—and what young person is without promise!—seem to have developed into great people only when they accepted the disciplines involved in continued personal effort.

This ability to accept challenges is a trait and technique our first group of American astronauts share with great scientists. These daring adventurers into space have won the world's admiration not alone for their breath-taking mastery of equipment scientists created for their use but for the mental and physical disciplines they had the courage and ability to undergo in order to achieve what they wanted to do.

It is men like these who, in every generation, continue to prove that those who planted the seeds of freedom from which our American democracy and heritage have grown were right in their conviction that all men are made in their Creator's image. Truly a little spark of greatness is the birthright of humanity. And no one can foresee the extent of the adventures into greatness which lie ahead for young people today who seek and accept challenges that confront them—accept them with the disciplines that lead to achievement.

EDNA YOST

CONTENTS

◆

MODERN AMERICANS
IN
SCIENCE AND TECHNOLOGY

ELMER A. SPERRY

GEORGE WASHINGTON CARVER

LEO HENDRIK BAEKELAND

WILLIS H. CARRIER

CHARLES F. KETTERING

FREDERICK G. COTTRELL

ROBERT R. WILLIAMS

EMIL TRUOG

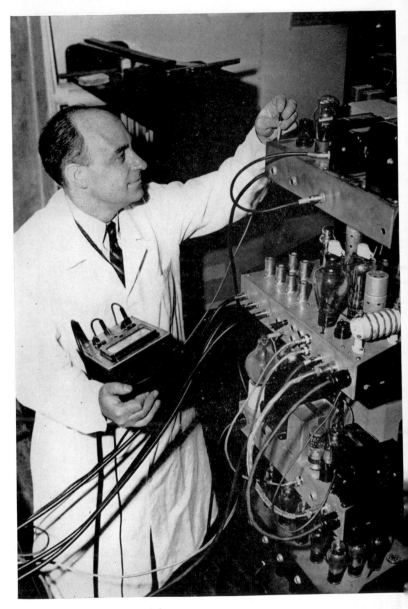

ENRICO FERMI

ROBERT HUTCHINGS GODDARD

U. S. Army Photograph

PAUL ALLMAN SIPLE

VLADIMIR K. ZWORYKIN (left)

JOHN P. HAGEN

ELMER A. SPERRY

(1 8 6 0 – 1 9 3 0)

An Inventor Who, with His Sons, Made Gyroscope
and Automatic Pilot History

◆

Airplane pilots have to pass stiff examinations before
they receive their flyers' licenses. One type of pilot, though,
is excused from these examinations. He is called "Automatic
Pilot," and he sits in the cockpit with the human pilot. He
enables the human pilot to fly hundreds of miles in the
wished-for direction without so much as touching a hand to
the control column.

It may seem a far cry from that automatic pilot in the air
to rough weather on the Atlantic Ocean one day in the early
years of this century. But there is a close connection. On that
day, Elmer A. Sperry of Cleveland, Ohio, was thrown vio-
lently to the deck of a ship struggling through rough weather
on the Atlantic. When he had picked up his bruised and
badly shaken body, an idea that had been hovering on the outskirts of his mind for a long time had taken fast hold of him.

"Why not—" the idea said to him,—"why not take the lurching and rolling out of ships with gyroscopes? Why not make ocean travel comfortable?"

And, believe it or not, the Sperry Automatic Pilot that is part of the equipment of most large planes today was one of the results that grew out of Elmer Sperry's determination to free ships from the whims of storm-ridden seas.

After he got back to Cleveland that fall, he was too busy with his other inventions to give much time to the gyroscope idea. He already held scores of patents on machinery and apparatus used for electric lighting of cities and the electrical digging of coal. He was in the midst of difficult problems on a Sperry storage battery for electric automobiles, for at that time it seemed as if electrically driven rather than gasoline-driven automobiles might have the bigger future. He was working fourteen to sixteen hours per day and spending many of his nights on Pullman cars between Cleveland and Washington, Chicago, Kansas City and Buffalo. But in spare moments at home, he might be found sitting on the floor with his three boys about him, showing them the various ways in which they could feel gyroscopic force or see its effects.

One of those boys, Elmer Junior, who became an inventor in his own right, has told how his father would have him hold a bicycle upside down, then give the wheel a hard spin so that young Elmer could feel the pull of the wheel seeking to hold the position it had been in when it began to spin.

"The force I'd feel when I'd try to turn that spinning wheel from the direction it insisted upon keeping," he said, "was terrific to a ten-year-old. And Father would say, 'I want to make that force you are feeling perform work for people just as I am making electricity dig coal for people.' "

The boys were interested. Two of them, Lawrence and

young Elmer, had been born with strong inventive streaks just as their father had. All of them plied him with questions. They listened in fascination to his answers. Yes, he told them, many men had felt this force and dreamed about using it for the benefit of mankind. But although the Frenchman, Foucault, had made known his invention of the gyroscope in the 1850's, few men had attempted to put it to practical use. Possibly the juggler the boys had seen catching sharp-pointed knives was one of the few people who had made money by using the force created by swiftly rotating bodies. The juggler mystified his audience because he had learned to give knives, as he tossed them into the air, a twist and spin that held them pointing in one direction as they descended.

Elmer Senior used to spin tops with the boys to explain to them the law of rotating bodies—that, while the inert top falls over if you put it on end, the spinning top stands upright.

"The spinning top is obeying the law of rotating bodies," he explained and he put into simple words for them this law which states that a rotating body offers strong resistance to any force that tries to change its direction.

One day he brought home a tiny model of a gyroscope he had made—a toy, he called it. For many years he carried it about with him, even to Europe where he showed it to the owners of the Krupp works in Germany. (He showed a later toy model to Mussolini in Rome in 1927 and the Duce's eyes opened wide with interest when Mr. Sperry said, "The force you are feeling in your hand, Excellency, is stronger than the Rock of Gibraltar.") It consisted of a comparatively heavy wheel so constructed that its axis was free to rotate in any direction on a horizontal or any other plane as though independent of the laws of gravity.

Taking turns, the boys held the tiny model in their hands while the wheel was made to spin rapidly. This little wheel which, for the duration of its rapid spinning, so strongly resisted their efforts to turn it from its original direction, might almost have been the earth. For (1)—it was free in space as the earth was free; (2)—it was spinning rapidly as the earth spins rapidly on its axis on its way around the sun; and (3)—it was holding to a steady direction just as the earth everlastingly holds its axis pointing approximately toward the North Star.

These boys had a real vision even then of what their father was trying to accomplish, and some day, when they were old enough, they knew they would want to help him achieve it. They saw clearly the two main things that were to be accomplished: first, the force created by a spinning body was to be used in a gyroscopic apparatus—a stabilizer that would make ships resist the efforts of the waves to roll them; second, the unswerving direction held by a spinning body in space was to be used in a gyroscopic compass that would be superior to the far-from satisfactory magnetic compasses universally in use.

Both Lawrence and Elmer Junior would have preferred to be immediately in their father's laboratory and shop. Erasmus High School in Brooklyn where the Sperrys had moved so that Elmer Senior could be near the Navy Yard for his gyroscopic work, seemed pretty dull. But to school they went! And their father, at the suggestion of Navy officers, decided to give his first attention to making a gyrocompass before he continued his work on a stabilizer.

Mariners had always had difficulty keeping their directions accurate with magnetic compasses because they were affected not only by the earth's magnetism but by the steel in a ship's construction. The bigger the ship, the more liable its compass became to error because of the greater mass of steel in the ship's construction. Particularly on a battleship, the turning of massive gun turrets made a magnetic compass very erratic. So Sperry set to work to make a compass that would be entirely independent of the earth's magnetic field and of the mass of steel in a warship. His first experimental gyrocompass was tested successfully on the battleship, the *Delaware*, in 1911. Today practically every vessel that goes to sea uses the gyrocompass. It has been acclaimed as the greatest navigational advance of the twentieth century.

Returning to his stabilizer work, it soon became evident to Mr. Sperry that, if the gyroscope he was designing and building was to succeed in keeping a boat steady, it would really take two gyroscopes to do it—a big one and a little one. So he made a big gyroscope with a small, free gyroscope beside it which picked up the first faint motion induced when a wave tried to lift one side of the ship. This baby gyro immediately started a motor which so manipulated the big gyro that it spun in the direction necessary to counteract the impending roll. Dealing in this way with each wave in turn, the ship was never permitted to build up a large roll which is the cumulative effect of several waves.

All of this seems simpler to people today than it did to Elmer Sperry in 1913 when he was installing his first stabilizer on the U.S. destroyer, the *Worden*, in the Brooklyn Navy Yard. He had plenty of trouble, after the huge mechanism had been designed, built and installed, in getting the stabilizer finely adjusted to the particular length and period of roll of the *Worden*. This was a difficulty that would have to be met each time a new stabilizer was built because each boat has its own individual roll.

It became increasingly apparent that gyroscopic stabilizers were going to be very expensive luxuries. Once Mr. Sperry had demonstrated how well they worked, he found a few millionaires who gave him contracts to build stabilizers for their yachts. These light-weight boats are used for pleasure, and they become very unpleasurable in rough weather. But passenger liners were being built bigger and heavier and therefore rode the waves more steadily. Their owners did not feel like investing a million dollars in equipment that would be needed for passenger comfort for comparatively short periods of time and only during stormy voyages. The 42,000 ton Italian liner, *Conte di Savoia,* was the only big passenger liner that was ever equipped with a gyroscopic stabilizer. It had three rotors, each of them weighing 108 tons. Other installations were made in submarines and airplane carriers as well as in yachts—forty-two in all; and an improved version of Sperry's original stabilizer has been designed for our nuclear submarines.

One of the most useful of all Sperry inventions is an automatic steerer which is found on most large merchant ships today. "Metal Mike," as the instrument is called, is a device joined to a gyrocompass which, when set in a certain direction, will hold a ship more accurately in that direction than the human hand can hold it. Just one of those simple little gadgets pilots and passengers alike quickly learn to take for granted! But it took inventive genius and engineering skill to produce it. The two Elmers, father and son, put the finishing touches on "Metal Mike" several years after the younger Elmer had left his engineering course at Cornell (he had completed in approximately two years what is regularly done in four) and had worked for the period of World War I on dangerous experiments undertaken by the Sperry organization in Brooklyn for the Army and Navy.

Meanwhile, Lawrence had refused to go to college and had immersed himself in the problems of stabilizing airplanes. That was a job of some magnitude, considering the weight involved in stabilizing equipment and the fact that earlier planes were having difficulties in raising even their own weight off the ground. With his father's help, Lawrence directed his efforts toward trying to make a gyroscopic stabilizer light enough and small enough for a cockpit, yet able to handle the extra motions—up and down and all the tipping resulting therefrom—which an airplane has in addition to the forward and backward motion of a ship.

Lawrence's career was brief but brilliant. It focused on flying. When he and Elmer were still in Erasmus High, they built an airplane that succeeded in covering the field out at the Sheepshead Bay Race Track in a series of hops. Fear seemed to be left out of Lawrence's make-up, and his desire to be in the air rather than in engineering school was too strong for his father and mother to turn aside. So, while his younger brother was finishing at Exeter and Cornell, Lawrence was in the air. In 1914 he sailed for France with a Curtiss flying boat for luggage. On it was a Sperry stabilizer. France had offered a prize of 25,000 francs for a stable airplane and Lawrence was on his way.

Fifty-three contestants competed in that unique contest. Lawrence Sperry took first prize. With his father and mother both watching him, he flew so low that the crowd on the field could see him with both hands raised from the control apparatus. As the plane was about to pass the judge's stand, Lawrence's dare-devil French mechanic climbed out of the cockpit and stood on the wing, demonstrating the ability of the gyrostabilizer to counteract the upsetting force of his weight.

It was a wonderful success for so young a man. But no one realized better than he how much remained to be done to make flying safe and practical. It was going to take a lot of work to improve airplane engines and other instruments, as well as a stabilizer, to overcome the tremendous hazards involved in cross-country flying in which all sorts of weather conditions would be encountered. For nine more years, Lawrence Sperry used his brilliant inventive mind and his fearless body to take the hazards out of flying for coming generations. Then, one day in December 1923, engine trouble caused a forced landing in the English Channel. A good swimmer, Lawrence struck out for the shore, but he did not make it. The icy water of the Channel was too much for him.

Some time after Lawrence's death, his brother took up his work where he had left it. The result, eventually, was the Sperry Automatic Pilot. It became world famous in the early 1930's when Wiley Post, shortly after returning from his trip around the world with Harold Gatty, took off on a solo flight to cover the same ground with only a Sperry Automatic Pilot for company. Post flew all the way around the world again and when he returned, he reported that he had had plenty of time for rest, map-reading and radio manipulation, while his automatic pilot did the necessary work.

To Lawrence Sperry goes credit for having influenced his father's work as well as having been strongly influenced by it. During the years when Lawrence was flying everywhere and in everything available, his father was engaged in several fields of invention other than aviation or the application of the principle of the gyroscope. In this period he returned to the field of electric lighting, in which he had started his career, to make a brilliant contribution. This was a searchlight five times as bright as any that had existed heretofore.

The high intensity Sperry searchlight, as it was called, came in time to influence military tactics before the end of World War I. These powerful lights were used by both the U.S. Army and Navy. Rushed to the front in Europe, their immediate effect was to permit night-flying enemy planes to be spotted and become targets for anti-aircraft batteries. They were standard military equipment until near the end of World War II when radar came into general use, and were adopted early by the motion picture industry for studio lighting and projection.

Only a few years before Mr. Sperry's death, he made an invention which has become, possibly, his greatest contribution to human safety. This was the Sperry Detector Car which is now in continuous operation on practically all railroad tracks in the United States and Canada. Nothing demonstrates the versatility of its inventor's genius better than does this idea, late in his life, which solved a problem that had plagued and baffled railroad officials for decades and was growing greater with each passing year. The problem was that internal flaws in rails, invisible to the eye, frequently developed after continuous use. They weakened the rail until, at some moment of stress, a break occurred which could cause a serious accident and, often, death.

Despite improvements in rail manufacture, these internal flaws kept occurring, and by 1927 railroad men were very much discouraged about finding a solution. At a meeting of high rail officials that year, Mr. Sperry proposed a solution. It was his belief that if a low-voltage heavy current were passed through a rail, any hidden fissure would cause an obstruction which would produce a voltage change by which the location of the fissure could be detected. Within a year he had built his first Detector Car, and it spotted fissures! By the early 1960's, more than a million defective rails had been detected. The cars have feeler coils beneath them which are carried just above the rail head, and every time a fissure is found a spot of white paint is squirted against the rail at the exact location of the flaw. Sometimes the rails at these spots are so weak they break, revealing the fissure when a maintenance crew removes them.

The recipient of many honors bestowed upon him in Europe, Asia and America and with four hundred patents to his credit, Elmer Sperry died in 1930, leaving Elmer Junior to carry the Sperry name to a new niche in American science and technology. That is a story in itself, one with no place here. But it gives added validity to the assertion that this has been a wonderful family—this gyroscope family which found, in a spinning top, a challenge that opened up a whole new field of inventive achievement. And one of its most healthful and impressive aspects is that none of Elmer Sperry's sons, including Edward whose business abilities found expression in his father's company which he served as treasurer for many years, was content to ride to glory on his father's accomplishments.

GEORGE WASHINGTON CARVER

(1 8 6 4 – 1 9 4 3)

Wizard of Tuskegee Who Made Peanuts a Valuable Crop for Southern Farmers

◆

Some time along toward the end of the Civil War a frail, sickly child was born of a slave woman on the plantation of Moses Carver in Missouri. As was the custom of the day, the child was given the surname of his master. When he was six weeks old and ill of whooping cough, he and his mother were stolen by a band of raiders who carried them off into captivity. Eventually Moses Carver made contact with his slaves' captors and ransomed the sickly child for a racehorse worth about three hundred dollars. The mother was never found. That is all George Washington Carver ever knew about his parents except that his father, a slave owned by a neighbor of Moses Carver, was supposed to have been killed by an ox-team while hauling a load of wood.

That little child of slave parents became George Washington Carver, B.S., M.S., D.Sc., Ph.D., Fellow of the Royal Society of Arts, London and Director of Research and Ex-

periment at the Tuskegee Institute in Alabama. He was
ranked by his fellow American scientists as a great creative
chemist. His contributions in the realm of agricultural chemistry were of outstanding value throughout the world, but
particularly to our own South. They won for him offers of
positions at fabulous salaries. Thomas A. Edison once suggested that his good friend Carver could use his expert knowledge at a salary many times what Tuskegee was paying him,
on a special piece of research at the Edison laboratories in
New Jersey. One offer is reported to have had a salary of
$100,000 a year attached to it. They seem not even to have
tempted him. Dr. Carver had found at Tuskegee a place
where he could use his every ability to serve his fellow man.
From his point of view, nothing else was important.

The story of Dr. Carver's struggle for an education matches
almost any struggle in the records. He was so frail a child that
it was important for him to find a way to earn a living which
did not involve hard manual labor. The Carvers approved
of school for this full-blooded little Negro, but there was no
school near enough their plantation for him to attend. So at
the age of only ten years he set out to make his way alone.

Mrs. Carver had taught him what she could. Under her
he had mastered his only textbook—a blue-backed speller. She
had trained him in housework for which it was apparent he
had great talent. He could not only do washing and ironing
and cleaning, but was an excellent cook and could sew and
mend to perfection. So, as he traveled off to seek a school
(and sleep in barns until he could find a way to earn his bed
and board) he took her training with him. It enabled him
from the beginning to support himself with the kind of work

he could do while he laid the foundations for the college education he soon had in mind.

When he had learned as much as he could in one school, he would move on to a town whose educational opportunities were greater. In this manner he eventually worked his way through a Kansas high school and was ready, intellectually, for college. His job now was to get enough money ahead to pay his tuition. This was not easy. For one thing, he was still very frail and undersized. When he was seventeen and had enough money to take a train trip back to visit Mr. and Mrs. Carver, he was almost refused permission to travel by train because the conductor thought he was too little to be taking so long a trip alone. Two years later he suddenly began to grow and at twenty-one had reached nearly six feet. This made him capable of heavier, harder work, but he had the kind of feeling about money that made him ask little for his labor and an independence that did not permit him to accept anything from anybody without earning it.

Competent as he was in many tasks, it was work with the earth—watching things grow up through the soil—that fascinated young Carver most. While other boys watched birds in flight and were enthralled by the mystery of how they flew, this child used to poke his fingers under a snowdrift to find the waxy blossoms of trailing arbutus, lost in wonder at what made the blossoms appear under the snow. Although he had never as a child been sent to Sunday School or given any religious training, he had already found, deep within himself, a religious feeling about the simplicities of nature and a belief that God was present in his—George Washington Carver's—fumbling efforts to understand their meaning.

In some such spirit as this, he worked and saved his tiny

sums and set out for the agricultural college he had decided to attend, which had accepted his application for entrance. Unfortunately he had to spend a good part of his tuition money in order to get there. Then, when they saw his color, they refused him. Shocked and saddened, he wandered off, and in Ness County, Kansas, he filed a claim for a homestead, built himself a little sod house and got a job doing housework at a livestock ranch nearby, which financed the crops he wanted to put in.

This was the first of the many agricultural experiments that were to fill his life and it was a failure. From this experience he learned that soil can be satisfactory for grazing herds and still be a failure in its immediate crop yield. But he earned and saved despite his experience with the soil, and when he had tuition money again, he set off for Indianola, Iowa, to enroll at Simpson College, which he had been told would accept him as a student.

This was a happier experience. He was accepted, found work in the college laundry, and not only earned his own way but had saved a little money by the time he graduated at the end of three years. He had not only taken the college work required but had studied music and art as well. Actually he had talents both as a pianist and painter that could have probably made him successful, in either of these fields.

But Simpson had not given him the agricultural course he wanted most, so now he set out for the Iowa Agricultural and Mechanical College at Ames, arriving with money for his tuition and ten cents left over. The director of the Agricultural Experiment Station at Ames at that time was Professor James Wilson who later served for a long period as Secretary of the U.S. Department of Agriculture in Washington. Learning of Carver's financial situation and knowing he would have a difficult time, even if he had money, to find a room on the college campus, he told the young Negro to sleep in his office if he wanted to. Carver matriculated, then bought five cents' worth of meal and five cents' worth of suet, which fed him for a week. By the end of that time he had found work. In three years, at the age of thirty, he received his B.S. in Agriculture and was placed in charge of the research in systematic botany and work in the college greenhouses. The latter gave him added inspiration for his paintings of flowers.

These assignments pleased him greatly. He was pursuing his own investigations, deepening his knowledge of natural products of the soil and studying for his Master of Science degree. Two years passed. Then, at just about the time he was finishing the requirements for his M.S., the head of Tuskegee Institute in Alabama, Booker T. Washington, suggested that he come to Tuskegee to develop a much needed department of agriculture there. This seemed to Mr. Carver to be where he belonged, and he never changed that opinion. Nor did he stray from the star he set out to follow from the moment he first walked into the old building, all but completely devoid of equipment, which was to be his laboratory.

The story of the man who grew to be called the "Wizard of Tuskegee" begins now, in 1896, with his gathering a few students about him and taking them through the alleys and back streets of a sleepy Alabama town to collect bottles and jars, bits of rubber and wire, any odds and ends his long, slender fingers might fashion into laboratory equipment. He then took over nineteen of the worst acres in Alabama to use as an experiment station to prove that coarse sand, fine sandy loam and clay could be treated and worked at a profit. At the end of twelve months, one of those acres that had cost a sixteen dollar loss the year before had grown crops showing a four dollar profit. In seven years he was able to produce a seventy-five dollar profit on an acre of sandy loam and the very next year to raise a five hundred pound bale of cotton on it, an accomplishment hitherto possible only on the very best Alabama soil.

Even before the boll weevil arrived in Alabama in the late 1890's to cause almost total destruction of the cotton crop, Dr. Carver had seen farmers of the South grow poorer and poorer because they failed to use the simplest scientific methods such as intelligent rotation of crops to keep their soil properly productive. With the arrival of the boll weevil he saw them faced with bankruptcy. When he was appealed to for suggestions as to how to stave off complete ruin, "Raise peanuts," he advised. Boll weevils would not attack peanuts, and he knew peanuts would grow in soil that grew cotton.

Soon farmers throughout the South were raising a new type of crop, but what was the good of raising peanuts if they could not sell them? Dr. Carver had helped them solve one kind of an agricultural-economic problem only to have them faced with another one. So now he set about the particular work for which he is most famous. He used his laboratory at Tuskegee to experiment with ways in which the peanut might become a profitable crop. He discovered nearly three hundred uses to which it could be put, and the peanut crop that had once been negligible grew, in his lifetime, to have five million acres allotted to it on Southern farms and an annual value of $200,000,000.

Shortly after he had suggested that Southerners use their

cotton land for growing peanuts, he urged that sweet potatoes, too, be grown in greater quantities. He then did for the sweet potato what he was doing successfully for the peanut. He revealed new uses to which it could be put until it, too, became an agricultural crop of considerable value. Some of the products he made out of peanuts were: milk, butter, cheese, candies, instant coffee, pickles, oils, sauces, shaving lotions, wood stains, dyes, lard, linoleum, flour, breakfast food, soap, face powder, tan remover, shampoo, printer's ink and axle grease. Out of the sweet potato he created more than one hundred products, including flour, meal, starch, library paste, vinegar, shoeblacking, ginger, ink, rubber and chocolate compounds, dyes, molasses, wood fillers and caramels.

It is interesting to know Dr. Carver's explanation of how he was able to do these things which science today calls "creative chemistry." He had formed the habit, he said, of getting up very early in the morning and going out-of-doors to walk in the woods before he started his work for the day. In these early morning hours he would ask God questions about his work and receive the guidance that enabled him to achieve the results he accomplished. When, for example, he found that many farmers had taken his advice and grown peanuts and then were faced with the possibility of hungry children because they could not sell their crops, he was greatly troubled because he felt his responsibility in the matter. So he asked God in one of his morning walks what he could do about it and the answer came, "Find new uses for the peanut. Break it up and see what it is made of. Then find uses based upon its different elements." Morning after morning he would walk in the woods and plan his day's work. Then he would go to his laboratory or his acres and pursue the scientific methods he had learned in college and kept developing over the years.

Naturally, some scientists smiled and said that Dr. Carver's daily "communing with God" was more superstitious than scientific. But that attitude belonged more to a day when a greater gulf appeared to separate science and religion than appears, in the minds of some of our great scientists, to separate them today. Every great scientist knows the value of a "hunch" in the midst of a problem, although few would define accurately just what a hunch is. They all know that, in the midst of a piece of work, a sudden suggestion may suddenly come to a man's mind telling him to try a certain something next, and he may try it. The history of science is full of incidents where whole years of work have been climaxed by the following of a hunch. The scientist to whom this happens may not think of his "hunch" as being connected with God's guidance. But he recognizes that a suggestion "flashed into his mind" which he cannot explain logically.

Dr. Carver did not permit his daily habit of asking questions of God to interfere with the scientific methods he pursued in his laboratory. He used it, instead, as an aid in directing disciplined mental efforts later in the day. In this, he followed the technique of many successful men who, when they first waken, lie quietly and let ideas run through their minds without trying to do any logical thinking. Often they get some of their best ideas at this time. Far from being a superstitious practice, this is a technique that has often brought success to the creative worker.

Dr. Carver called his practice "talking with God," and it may be that in his willingness to speak of it so simply and frankly he has made a valuable contribution to young people who are to be our scientists and creative workers of tomorrow. He did not suggest that young people should go on morning walks and talk with God. But he did emphasize that in solitude the scientific mind achieves something which, added to what it gains through disciplined methods of science, is greater than it could achieve through either method alone. He found that just as a person usually accomplishes most when he forms the habit of regular hours of work, so the period of solitude is most productive when it comes regularly at an appointed time.

Certainly the proof of the pudding is in the eating, and Dr. Carver, through his methods, made outstanding contributions in the field of agricultural chemistry. He was called upon time and again to solve some knotty problem troubling a group of individuals or a foreign government. A group from Canada came to him to learn how acres of sunflowers could be converted into chemical products. Another group from Oklahoma wanted to know how an acid-sludge residue from a large mineral oil property might be utilized profitably. Another group in Hawaii wanted help in eliminating a disease attacking pineapples. In so far as he had time, he tackled the problems one by one. Often he solved them. And if anyone misunderstood his motives enough to send him a check, he returned it with an explanation that he was sincerely interested in problems that touched the lives and happiness of human beings, but had no desire to make money out of them. His modest living at Tuskegee gave him everything he needed.

In 1928 the Crown Prince of Sweden spent several weeks with Dr. Carver getting valuable information for his country concerning methods of converting agricultural substances into raw materials for industry. Men of science, including Julian Huxley, spent fascinated hours with him in his laboratory, oblivious to the patched blue apron covering his patched homespun suit—a suit made from materials he himself had converted into cloth after he had gathered them up in his rambles through fields and woods. Tramping about from laboratory shelves to window ledges in a pair of shoes so patched that possibly none of their original leather remained, he held his visitors intent by the wizardry of his intellect.

No story of the life of this scientist should omit recognition of the fact that he was an artist too. As a younger man, he was accomplished enough as a pianist to make a concert tour of the Middle West. His strong hands with their long, slender fingers often made people think of other musicians' hands they had seen. They were more, though, than the hands of a musician and scientist. They created pictures of such beauty that the Luxembourg Gallery in Paris tried to buy one of them. Dr. Carver did not wish to sell it, but he arranged for it to be a gift after his death. It is the picture of a rose, and represents the artist's idea of the "Infinite Mind" with which he communed daily and which helped him use his talents in science for the good of mankind, especially of the South he loved.

The Carver pictures are unique in that all the paints he used on them were created by him from Alabama soils. Visitors to his office were often struck by the reproductions of Maxfield Parrish paintings on the walls. The blues for which Parrish is famous were especially pleasing to Dr. Carver. He himself worked on the creation of blue pigments for years and out of Alabama's mountainsides he brought soils to his test tubes and retorts that yielded color after color of astounding beauty, including one particular blue which he thought might be a rediscovery of the old Egyptian blue which modern pigment makers have been unable to reproduce.

But the self-expressive creation of beauty, whether in music, painting or the exquisite embroideries and crochet work he did, was not of as much importance to Dr. Carver as was the work he could see bringing beneficial results into the lives of his fellow human beings. Throughout the South, thousands of farmers are growing more abundant crops today because he showed them or their fathers how to go to the swamps and gather up free leaves and muck and make a compost that is hard to beat as a soil builder. This was the kind of demonstration that brought increasing joy to his heart as long as he lived. He wanted his work to give people everywhere, but especially in his own South, a more abundant life.

His scientific work was, of course, somewhat limited in scope. It was thorough in a limited field rather than scattered over a wider field. There were some who criticized it by asking if there is any real value in knowing so many hundreds of uses for a few agricultural products. Dr. Carver was always undisturbed by this type of question. The pursuit of truth, he knew, was the most valuable occupation in the world, even though practical demonstrations of its values are slow in being made. Before his death in 1943, he had the satisfaction of knowing nutrition experts were vigorously stressing the value of peanut butter in a good diet, especially for children, though he himself did not know its nutritional values when he urged farmers to grow peanuts.

Dr. Carver lived and died in the faith that all truth has value, and that some of the truths he unearthed held values that would bring benefit to human beings after he was gone from this earth. Certainly he stimulated his students at Tuskegee to continue to serve the South by revealing more of the truth about what can be done with her climate and soil. For the length of his own life, he served both the South and the world well and he did so with the kind of humility that is the earmark of true greatness.

LEO HENDRIK BAEKELAND

(1863–1944)

Creator of Bakelite Plastics, Foundation Stone beneath a Great New Twentieth Century Industry

◆

Hɪs ɴᴀᴍᴇ was Baekeland, and his great achievement is now called bakelite. When he first created this now world-famous plastic, he took out his pencil and notebook and counted up forty-three industries that he thought might be able to use his product. Today it is hard to name a business or industry that does not use plastics.

Bakelite—or bakelite phenolic resinoid, to be technically accurate—was the foundation stone of this great new industry unknown before the early years of the present century. It may not employ as many men as our biggest industries, but it permeates into so many of them that its indirect wage-roll is enormous. It was first made possible through the work of a chemist who learned how to combine formaldehyde (a gas derived from methyl alcohol) with phenol (carbolic acid) to form a resin-like substance of great strength, non-porosity and hardness.

23

This chemist, Leo Hendrik Baekeland, born in the Flemish city of Ghent, Belgium, was only eight years old when his schoolteacher told him the story of Benjamin Franklin, the first American scientist. He did not dream at that time that he was going to choose to become an American, but he did know early in life that he had an interest in science. He attended the free evening lectures at the Ghent Municipal Technical School (an institution resembling Cooper Union in New York City) when he was in his early teens and a day student at the Royal Athenæum, a government high school. At seventeen, he entered the University of Ghent as the youngest student in his class. From this time on he not only completely supported himself by tutoring and as a lecture assistant in chemistry, but he also took his degrees in record time. At twenty, he won his Bachelor of Science degree and at twenty-one received his Doctorate in Science after passing the examinations with highest honors. That was in 1884.

In those days the four Belgian universities of Ghent, Liège, Brussels and Louvain held a competition every three years among their graduates of that period. In the competition of 1887, Dr. Baekeland, by that time an assistant professor of chemistry, won first prize in chemistry, for which the award was a gold medal and funds for a traveling scholarship which enabled him to visit universities in Germany, France, Scotland and England. The trip whetted his interest in further education by travel, and he decided to follow up his visit through Europe and the British Isles with a trip to the United States in 1889.

During his years of teaching, he had continued the work in photography in which he had first become interested as a young student in Ghent, a city that had become the center of the exciting new industry of dry-plate manufacture. He was an enthusiastic amateur photographer and was not unknown to people interested in the new branch of the chemical industry related to it. It was quite natural, therefore, that one of the first things he did upon arriving in New York was to call upon H. T. Anthony and Company which, through later mergers, became part of the Agfa Ansco Company with which modern photographers are familiar. They happened to be needing a chemist who was familiar with photography and photo chemicals and offered Dr. Baekeland the position. He promptly accepted it, and when his resignation from his university position was received, the Minister of Education for Belgium paid him the unusual compliment of authorizing him to retain the honory title of Associate Professor of the University of Ghent.

After two years in America he had so many ideas of his own he wanted to develop that he resigned his position with the Anthony firm to establish himself as a consulting research chemist, with opportunity for time to work on some of his own projects. Like many another man young enough and strong enough to think he can overwork for long periods with impunity, he undertook too many things at once. In a surprisingly short time he ended up with a severe illness that kept him hovering between life and death for a while, took all his cash, put him in debt and knocked a new kind of common sense into his head. In a heart-to-heart session with himself as soon as he was physically able, he decided to concentrate on one single piece of work that would give him best chances for quick results. His choice, after weighing the facts, was to return to his first love, photography, especially to a kind of photo-printing paper he had worked on in his student days in Ghent.

In the early 1890's photographers used the slow and unreliable "sun printing" method. If, as happened often, the sun did not appear for days, the photographer did not print pictures and the customer waited. (Imagine a modern newspaper doing that today!) Baekeland's paper—Velox—was to use artificial light instead of sunlight and be very much speedier than papers then in use.

The great chemical difficulty that stood in the way lay mainly in making a chloride of silver for commercial purposes in the preparation of photographic emulsions. Baekeland did not know at that time that it was going to be much of a difficulty. The problem of a chemical reaction to produce a silver chloride looked very simple in the textbooks. The classroom authorities had already established that there were three or four different varieties of silver chloride, all of the same chemical composition but differing in their physical properties, and Baekeland anticipated no real snags. But, as he began to try to make classroom chemistry meet commercial needs, he discovered there were perhaps a hundred varieties of silver chloride, only one of which had a chance of keeping him out of the poorhouse.

Eventually he found the chloride he was after. Eventually, too—though not during the months of his research which produced one disheartening failure after another—he was able to count the experience as good luck. For he had learned the lesson of the endless detail, of the long years of research, of failure and beginning all over again, which the chemist must learn to go through with if he is to bring a chemical process from its textbook and laboratory stage to successful commercial application. He was not again to be severely tempted to begin too many projects at once after this type of experience.

He had more luck when, at just about the time he had Velox ready for the public, a friend appeared who was willing to put up the money for its manufacture on a commercial scale. But this was in 1893, a year of severe economic depression and one in which unexpected technical troubles were going to arise for Baekeland because of climatic conditions in the United States. Manufacturers of photo-printing paper in Europe, where the amount of moisture in the air does not vary to such an extraordinary extent between seasons, were not meeting the problems that now had to be met in the United States, where air is so dry in winter as to cause electric sparks and in the summer often so saturated with moisture that machinery and other objects condense water on their surfaces at temperatures as high as 76° F. Unfortunately, Willis Carrier had not yet come along with his air-conditioning apparatus, but if he had, surely no one would have welcomed him with arms wider open than the harassed Baekeland who, on top of everything else, had to solve the problem of moisture control by a refrigerating machine that extracted some of the moisture from the air. Dr. Baekeland said later he believed that some American industries reached a high degree of development and perfection sooner than similar industries in Europe because our air-moisture conditions compelled early solving of problems that could be postponed in Europe.

With the moisture problem for the manufacture of his photo-printing paper eventually solved and the financial problem temporarily eased, it should have been smooth sailing. But it was not. The public refused to think that artificial light, for which Velox had been created, should be used for photo printing. Professional photographers in particular were set in their routine of sun-printing. So they insisted on using Velox in that way and then condemning it heartily as a failure.

"You claim your method is several hundred times faster than albumen paper and here I have kept a print in the printing frame for several hours and can hardly see a faint image," one photographer wrote. And those words described failures experienced by hundreds of people who either did not read or did not believe the directions for printing "in artificial light only" that accompanied every package of Velox.

Actually it was the amateur photographers who gave Baekeland his break eventually. They were willing to be taught and they were responsible, in large measure, for the early success of Velox. The man who worked all day and did not have the sun at night time when he was free to follow his hobby was the one who was glad to follow directions about artificial light. Before long he was showing his friends better prints than their photographer was able to show them, prints that did not fade as easily either. The new paper began to catch on. A couple of years more and Velox was so well established that, in 1899, the Eastman Kodak Company took it over on very liberal terms, which relieved Dr. Baekeland from earlier financial worries and left him free to devote some time to new studies and research.

But—and this in his estimation was of first importance—only through devoting himself wholeheartedly to a valuable process, and seeing it through its experimental stages into the period when it was of immediate commercial value in an established industry, did he buy the freedom which the true scientific research man wants more than business success and the accumulation of a fortune. He had learned enough to know that the castle-in-the-air stage when so many chemists think their processes are ready for sale, is not one when a hard-headed business man can afford to take them over at the handsome figures their creators ask. Difficulties and expense cannot be foreseen accurately before a process is put to practical commercial-size application.

Six years passed. In this period Dr. Baekeland did important chemical work in establishing some of our big industries growing up around Niagara Falls where the electricity developed by the waters of Niagara was beginning to be utilized on a large scale. He studied for a winter at Charlottenburg, Germany, in the electrochemical laboratory of the technological institute there, and built and equipped for himself a laboratory adjoining his home in Yonkers upon his return to America. His association with the Niagara industries had been very profitable and by 1905 he was able to undertake the project that was to be the crowning achievement of his life—his research into methods of creating synthetic resins, which was to produce bakelite.

It was no haphazard choice or accident that made him determine to undertake this work. He had learned a lot about himself by the time he was forty. He knew that he had great powers of concentration, that he could so immerse himself in a problem for years that even a brief vacation forced upon him by a watchful wife was irksome simply because it removed him from his favorite problem. Once its solution had been found he knew he could go off and relax thoroughly, lose interest in what had been occupying his mind for so long and be ready to take up something new. He had also learned—and this was important—that a problem which had roused his innate interest and enthusiasm was, regardless of its financial prospects at the moment, the one on which he could do his best work. Now, because of its innate interest for him, and because he had the financial independence to do pretty much as he wanted, he turned to a problem that had fascinated but baffled many chemists before him—the creation of a synthetic resin that could improve many industrial products.

The type of resin he was after was a thermo*setting* plastic— that is, a substance which sets into permanent shape and will not soften under heat. The thermo*plastic* type—one that softens under reheating—had been known for more than thirty years, ever since John Hyatt started to manufacture celluloid, which he had created by combining a cellulose nitrate with camphor and alcohol. It had been known for approximately this same period of time, too, that resins could be obtained by combining an aldehyde (a substance obtained from alcohol) with phenol, better known as carbolic acid. Many interesting substances had resulted as various chemists tried again and again to create a usable synthetic resin in this way.

Scientists knew there was a law that governed the results they were getting. The trouble was, the results were usually intractable masses, abandoned eventually as giving no promise for industrial use and so diverse they concealed the law that governed them. Very definitely, though, resins could be formed which possessed qualities entirely different from the properties of the substances used in creating them.

The one thing that certainly did not result, when the aldehyde and carbolic acid were "married" in Baekeland's Yonkers laboratory, was the substance later known as bakelite or anything comparable to it. But as Baekeland experimented with one fusion after another, he eventually knew he was not after the type of resin nature creates and earlier chemists had probably sought. He was hunting a super-resin that would be infusible, insoluble, resistant to acids and oils. He wanted a substance usable as a gum but also usable as an indestructible solid.

The technical difficulties encountered before he achieved what he was willing to call bakelite would need an expert chemist to describe them intelligently, and other expert chemists to read about them intelligently. For the expert chemist who had determined to solve them, they necessitated many months of minute attention to detail and new ideas that took him step after step through baffling failures on his way to success. Eventually the day arrived on which the miracle was about to happen. On that day, as Dr. Baekeland applied greater heat, then counterpressure as the greater heat increased the chemical activity, he saw the liquid in the glass receptacle change into what looked like a beautiful transparent piece of amber. It took the shape of the receptacle in which it had been born and, on cooling, fell out with a perfect glossy surface.

From that moment on the success of the new resinlike material was assured. No chance, now, for it to elude the wizard chemist who had produced it. Many problems remained to be conquered (that first amber substance, for instance, was quite brittle) but the heart of the secret had yielded itself and the new world of plastics was about to become Dr. Baekeland's oyster.

Once the initial laboratory work was far enough along, he installed a small manufacturing unit where he could produce his material in ton lots under all kinds of conditions. He knew from experience that manufacture on a commercial scale would develop surprises and he wanted to meet as many of them as possible on a small scale first. Then he found potential users who put his product to the test of practical application in specific industries. Those days—approximately 1909—saw the beginning of the plastics industry in this country and in the world, with the manufacture of less than twenty-five barrels of bakelite in Yonkers. Dr. Baekeland and his chemists had learned how to control the chemical reactions in his process so that any given result could be achieved over and over again, which meant that production on a greater commercial scale could be undertaken.

At this point Dr. Baekeland had again to exercise precaution about not stepping out in too many directions at once. His product quickly offered a diversity of uses, but he soon found that unless he himself kept close supervision over its manufacture, chemical details which seemed simple to him were overlooked and the plastic did not live up to expectations. Chemists had to be trained who could be responsible for absolute uniformity of product.

He forced himself, in those early days, to concentrate on certain lines of work. At first he made the mistake of trying to make the plastic so he could sell it as cheaply as possible. Soon he learned it was not the price but the "super" qualities of which the new product was capable that made it most desirable to industries. His success came by creating quality in his product and by learning how to provide it for use in industries in a state that did not demand too much skill and knowledge from the average workman.

Electrical manufacturers were the first to seize upon bakelite because of its superior qualities for insulation and its resistance to other bodies. Workmen in this industry used to working with rubber for insulation now had to be taught new tricks they found hard to learn. Rubber softened in heat and solidified by cooling, while the new plastic "froze" in heat and needed high temperatures to make it hard and strong. Often an inexperienced amateur learned the technique more quickly than the experienced worker who had first to unlearn the old ways. But bakelite materials were so superior to the old products on so many counts that, despite drawbacks, industries wanted it, and it made its way quickly. Each succeeding year found new manufacturers wanting to use it, and Dr. Baekeland and his chemists were kept busy creating forms of the material with specific qualities suited to new fields of use.

One of the most popular forms in which bakelite was made available was as a liquid. Today all plastics start out as liquids, pellets, granules or sheeting, from which they are made into everything from phonograph records to draperies or food bags, from squeeze bottles to boat hulls or automobile bodies. In the early days Dr. Baekeland provided a liquid form that could be made to replace many celluloid items which were great fire risks. This liquid could be heated to about 300° F. for a few hours, under pressure of 50 to 100 pounds per square inch and in molds of any shape wanted, and so be turned into a hard, strong, insoluble, infusible resinoid, light in weight but having a tensile strength of more than 7000 pounds per square inch cross section. It did not melt at any heat, although at very high temperatures it would begin to char. It came into great demand for cigarette holders and costume jewelry because of its elimination of the danger of fire.

Bakelite became and remained the trademark of plastics manufactured by the Bakelite Corporation, of which Dr. Baekeland served as president until after his seventy-fifth birthday. In more recent years, his Company became a part of the Plastics Division of the Union Carbide Corporation. Plastics today are a far bigger industry than bakelite and its products. Following publication of Dr. Baekeland's description of his phenolic plastic in 1909, thousands of chemists set to work and thousands of patents covering other processes resulted. Within twenty years, the scant twenty-five barrels of plastic produced in the manufacturing unit installed in the Yonkers laboratory had increased to about ten million pounds of many types of plastics produced in the United States. That figure had grown to more than four billion pounds by 1960.

Fourteen basic types of plastics with hundreds of variations are being made today. All of them start with such common resources as coal, petroleum, natural gas, air, water, sand or salt, from which chemical processes extract elements and then combine these elements into the materials Americans use and often waste thoughtlessly. Baekeland's phenolic type had started with coal, air and water which were converted into the carbolic acid and formaldehyde out of which he finally procured the first plastic.

Bakelite held its creator's interest as long as he lived. After his retirement in 1939 he found more time for yachting, which gave him great pleasure, but chemistry was his first and last great love. He was another of our successful, practical men of science who called attention to the fact—as Charles Kettering so often did—that the banking and economic structures of his day were slow to incorporate into themselves the kind of financing of new industries necessary for keeping pace with scientific and technological progress. Dr. Baekeland welcomed the trend among a few enlightened industrialists who, before his death in 1944, were spending more money to equip and operate laboratories well staffed with scientific workers. In them he saw hopeful signs that augured well for young scientific research workers of the future.

WILLIS H. CARRIER

(1876–1950)

The Man Who Learned How to Manufacture Indoor Weather

◆

Possibly no men have been more valuable in our economic life since the beginning of the Machine Age than those who have created new types of industry. Workmen have been thrown out of work by the hundreds of thousands because of the increasing use of all kinds of machinery in long established industries. But completely new industries have kept arising to re-employ many of these men.

Willis Carrier, more than any other single individual, created the air-conditioning industry. He learned how to manufacture weather and in doing so he revolutionized many other industries. Without control of indoor weather, airplanes, for example, could not be turned out in mass production. And this is but one of many industries that have been rendered more efficient by Willis Carrier's ability to look at a glass of ice water sweating in a warm room and keep thinking "why?" about that old, old phenomenon until he could understand the underlying reason well enough to put the principle beneath it to work for him.

Mr. Carrier became interested in the "why" of things when he was a small boy just beginning fractions. He had been born on a farm near Angola, New York, in 1876, an only child whose mother died when he was still a youngster. But she had been alive when his teacher in the little village school started him on the addition and subtraction of fractions. He learned the processes mechanically and, when his mother questioned him, was able to give the right answers. But she saw he did not understand why five-eighths minus one-fourth left three eighths, or why three-fifths less a third left four-fifteenths. So she produced a plate of apples and set the youngster to work with his penknife to show himself not just what the correct answer was but why, when the operation was applied to a plate of apples, it was the correct answer.

For a good many years young Carrier seemed to be slower than some of his schoolmates. He was more interested in doing a little bit of work with real understanding than in doing a whole page of problems mechanically. By the time he reached the Angola Academy, the habit of finding out the why of everything that interested him had become so natural that he had no trouble in catching up with his classmates and doing the amount of work they did—but in his own way. This habit never left him.

Machinery and mathematics were his favorite subjects at the Academy, and he hoped to continue them in college as soon as he had his diploma. But that year was 1893—a year of depression and threatening bank panic. The older Mr. Carrier carried a mortgage on his farm and was in great danger of losing it through foreclosure. So seventeen-year-old Willis fitted himself for a country schoolteaching job and helped his father save the farm. Then he went off to live with a stepbrother in Buffalo and to have a year at Central High there in preparation for college. In a competitive examination that year he won a state scholarship which paid his tuition for four years at Cornell. The young man who left for Ithaca that fall was twenty-one years old and had five dollars in his pocket.

Cornell had been established thirty years earlier by a man who believed that a poor boy should be given ways of providing himself with an education in technical subjects equal to the best the country offered. Willis Carrier was one of the boys who took advantage of Ezra Cornell's practical idealism. He financed himself, in addition to his scholarship, by tending furnaces, waiting on tables and cutting grass. A siege with typhoid fever in his junior year made things pretty tough for him both financially and in his studies. But he returned to college, took over a successful laundry business and graduated with his class. In his senior year he and a partner formed the Student Laundry Agency which became a permanent student money-maker at Cornell. Each earned close to a thousand dollars that year. Even with all this, Carrier found time for rowing, cross-country running and boxing. He liked to debate, too—to figure out the why of things in logical argument.

With his bachelor's degree of Mechanical Engineer in Electrical Engineering in his pocket and no definite urge to get himself placed in any specific type of industry other than one where he could use his education and ingenuity, he accepted a ten-dollar-a-week job with the Buffalo Forge Company, manufacturers of blacksmiths' hand forges, fans, pumps and ventilating machinery of the simpler types then in use. It did not seem to offer any unusual opportunities; but, from Willis Carrier's point of view, for a man to meet the opportunities all about him was more important than for him to rush about trying to happen upon the unusual. "Opportunity never knocks twice," the old proverb says. "Why should it?" Mr. Carrier always countered. "A man ought to hear and answer the first knock, and that knock comes no matter where he is."

So Willis Carrier answered the simple knocks on the door of a ten-dollar-a-week job in the way he had fitted himself to answer them. From eight to six on weekdays and eight to one on Saturdays, he worked on the problems his job presented, trying, as he solved them, to learn the why beneath them. It was not long before he became the company's trouble shooter and was sent to answer any problems that arose with their machinery either in the company's own shops or out in any industry where Buffalo Forge Company apparatus was being used.

It so happened that one day he was put on a job for a Brooklyn lithographing and publishing company. This company was doing printing in color, and on a humid summer day the weather affected the paper's size and texture so that the edges of the colors overlapped. If they did their color printing on a dry day, they had a good clean job, but if they had to do it on a hot damp day, they had a messy job. There was nothing very striking about that. Other companies had been having similar difficulties with color printing.

To many men of his day, this did not look like much of an opportunity. A man could not do anything about the weather, they said, and let it go at that. But to Carrier it was the challenge that directed the whole course of his life and later affected the lives of millions of people all over the world.

He knew, as so many engineers had known before him, that if he could cool the air in the plant sufficiently he would automatically reduce its moisture. Why? Because cold air holds less moisture than warmer air. So he tried at first to keep the air cool enough with coil upon coil of cold-water pipes. It took a great deal of coil to cool a very small amount of air. On a commercial scale this application was soon seen to be impractical.

Now let's ponder along with a mind like Willis Carrier's —a mind that could see a glass of ice water sweating in a warm room as a simple fact and finally set the principle beneath it to work for him. His mind was not one to which solutions came in a quick flash, but it could look at an old fact in a new way, even so old a fact as "it isn't the heat, it's the humidity."

Air is like a sponge, he knew. It is constantly trying to soak up as much moisture as it can hold. It can, however, hold only so much. Eventually it reaches a saturation point beyond which it cannot soak up another drop. The warmer the air, the more moisture it can hold. That, he knew, was why humidity can become so oppressive on a hot summer day. Over in Brooklyn it was holding so much moisture on certain days that the lithographing company had given him the nut to crack of making it drier. And his coils of pipe were not cracking it.

Yet the fact remained that air in the plant could be made drier if he could make it cooler. Air at zero temperature can hold only a minute quantity of water vapor. Conduct some of that zero air indoors and heat it to seventy degrees, place water where this cold dry air can reach it as it grows warmer, and it will quickly absorb sixteen times as much water vapor as it had been able to hold at zero. It is a simple matter to keep the air in a heated room from being too dry for health or comfort in cold weather. Merely place enough sources of water around and the air automatically solves the problem itself. But to reverse the process—to make air *give* up rather than *soak* up water—that was not so simple!

Carrier's mind kept coming back to the picture of moisture on the outside of a glass of ice water in a hot room. That moisture had been condensed out of the air surrounding the glass. Air had given up water. It is a queer kind of paradox, he recognized, that if you set a pan of water, of the temperature at which it comes from the faucet, in a warm room, the water evaporates (that is, the greedy air absorbs, or takes up, moisture) and the room atmosphere becomes more humid. But if you set a pan of ice water in a warm room, condensed moisture covers the exposed surface of the pan (that is, the air surrounding that surface gives up, rather than takes up, moisture) as long as the water remains cold enough. In short, the air is actually dried by cold water! If you could put enough cakes of ice in a warm room, you would dry the air until the ice had melted and the resulting water had warmed to the point where the air began to absorb it, or take it up.

It may make the mind of the layman dizzy just to think about it so hard, but what this thinking did to Willis Carrier's mind was quite different. Eventually he told himself that if you could spray the humid air in the lithographing plant with very cold water, the air would have millions of little globules of cold water to condense its moisture upon.

Instead of the comparatively small, cold surfaces of the pipe coils to condense upon, it would have many, many times as much cold surface, and the colder you kept the water spray, the drier the air would become, because the colder you made the air the less moisture it could hold.

To apply this principle obviously meant new machinery involving a sizable humidifier (a device to keep air moist) to serve as a dehumidifier in which the spraying could be accomplished. It meant, also, a new kind of ventilating system for the building. Good ventilation was to be achieved by keeping all the doors and windows shut, and that was another paradox the world would have to learn to accept. It is a lot easier for us to accept it now than it was back in 1902 when Willis Carrier designed and installed the first scientific air-conditioning system in a Brooklyn lithographing plant. And it worked!

In a rather short time he had grasped enough of the opportunities that had grown out of his ten-dollar-a-week job to have found the specific kind of engineering to which he wanted to devote his life. Under his leadership a whole new field of engineering was to be opened up—the field of air conditioning. While working out his ideas he had taken out some patents basic to the water-spray process of dehumidifying air and of cleaning it. These ideas he improved upon by another invention which gave "dew-point control"—a device which automatically regulated the humidity by controlling the temperature of the spray water. Thus he was enabling himself to manufacture indoor weather in which the air was cleaned and the temperature, humidity and air distribution were all controlled.

Before all this had been achieved, he had done something

else which, in some ways, is his greatest contribution to the science of engineering. A few paragraphs earlier the fact was mentioned that dry air, heated to seventy degrees, would hold sixteen times as much water as that same air at zero. Previous to Carrier's work, many laws governing the mixture of air and water vapor were known, but they had never been assembled and codified. Willis Carrier began to bring these laws together and, with his own experiments, he completed them. It was a far bigger job than it may sound here. But eventually he had discovered the laws of psychrometry and set up the "Rational Psychrometric Formulae." On one chart, on a single piece of paper, he codified the many variables. This chart, together with a paper presented to the technical world in 1911 at a national meeting of engineers, constitutes the basis for the science of air conditioning and its calculation.

By 1915 Carrier's work had reached the stage where he, with J. I. Lyle and several other engineers who had been working with him, formed the Carrier Engineering Corporation with a capital of $35,000. In ten or twelve years it had built itself into a corporation with a capitalization of more than a million and a half dollars, all out of surplus earnings. It was one of the spectacular business successes during the depression period of the 1930's that greatly needed new industries to relieve unemployment. Its continuing growth and success were due, in part, to the fact that Mr. Carrier possessed a combination of business ability of a high order and a dominant concern for research and invention.

In the history of industry, however, Willis Carrier stands out as the "father of air conditioning" in a technological rather than in a commercial sense. After his patents were well in hand a great deal of work remained to be done to enable the systems he installed to operate successfully, and he devoted his life primarily to technological problems. He also had to train men who, as he expressed it, had to learn to "see, feel, smell, taste and know air when they meet it in the dark." They had to be able to estimate to a hair's breadth every feature of the enclosure to be air-conditioned, including floors, ceilings, windows, materials used in construction, types of surface exposure, etc. To be an engineer specializing in air conditioning was no vocation for a dull head. The training of talented men in technological methods he had first to create and master for himself had to become one of Willis Carrier's important jobs if his systems were to meet the demands industry put upon them.

For twenty years after his first installation, air conditioning was used almost exclusively in industrial plants. Paper and textile mills, pharmaceutical plants, soap and rubber factories, film studios, breweries, bakeries and meat-packing establishments all profited by control of atmospheric conditions. Air conditioning for comfort in big buildings had to wait until, in the early 1920's, Mr. Carrier developed a centrifugal refrigerating machine which made this field possible. Before this, he had merely adapted the type of refrigeration then in use to furnish cooling for his water spray that dehumidified the air. But this type of refrigeration was not well adapted for cooling the great quantities of water necessary for making a large office building or theater comfortable. The first model of his centrifugal refrigerating machine produced seventy tons of refrigeration per day, which was the equivalent of the melting of one thousand tons of ice daily.

Theaters, which used to remain closed during summer months, were among his first customers when this new type of air conditioning was ready. It was introduced on Broadway in 1925 at the Rivoli, and other theaters quickly asked for it. When the RCA Building was erected in the 1930's, two 965-ton machines were installed. Rockefeller Center as a whole has refrigerating machines with a capacity of more than 22,000 tons and is the largest system in use anywhere.

The Carrier Corporation plant itself was one of the best salesmen for the industry in the days when air conditioning was still a novelty. When King Prajadhipok of Siam was in this country, he inspected the plant personally. The day was one of those sizzling hot and humid ones such as the King knew all too well in Siam. He stepped from his car into the tightly closed building, and before he left it he had ordered air-conditioning units for the King's and Queen's quarters in the royal palaces, and others for each of two royal theaters.

Needless to say, Willis Carrier never regretted that ten-dollar-a-week job that had sent him to Brooklyn one day as a trouble shooter, where he suffered from the same humidity that was spoiling color printing in a lithographing establishment. It took him a long time to develop the science of air conditioning to the place where it worked equally well in industrial plants and large office buildings and in small units servicing individual rooms. But his interest in it continued, and long before his death in 1950 he experienced the satisfaction of knowing how greatly human efficiency as well as efficiency in industrial processes had increased because of his work. Mass production as we know it today would be impossible without air conditioning. As one example, delicate wood and fabric parts used in making airplanes are so subject to swelling or shrinking because of moisture in the air, or the lack of it, that unless the parts are all cut under exactly the same atmospheric conditions, trouble arises when planes are exposed to varying weather. Human beings also, find themselves in trouble when exposed too long to adverse weather conditions. Often they lose their efficiency, with decreased work and increased accidents as a result. Air conditioning eases this problem, too.

Mr. Carrier had the additional satisfaction of knowing the benefits of his efforts were not confined to his own country. They reached all over the world. Carrier systems are found, to mention only a few, in the Imperial Hotel in Tokyo, the Bank of India in Bombay, the Macdonald House in Singapore, the Houses of Parliament in Canada, Egypt, India, Lebanon, Norway, Peru and South Africa, and on many large ocean liners.

With it all the "father of air conditioning" never lost his own ability to enjoy himself without its benefits. Up until quite late in his life he used to spend weeks in his hunting lodge in Canada, bucking cold winter woods as he rested up and gathered new vigor for the work he was always planning ahead.

CHARLES F. KETTERING

(1876–1958)

Whose Inventions Made This Year's Cars Better than Last Year's and Who Never Stopped Wondering What Makes Grass Green

◆

CHARLES F. KETTERING was the man who, more than any other single individual, made it possible to touch an electric starter and make a car go. His Delco system for starting, lighting, and ignition of automobiles alone give him high rank among American inventors, and he has many other contributions to the automobile industry to his credit. Yet it is possible that, in the years to come, the chlorophyll research project he established at Antioch College may prove to be of more importance in the lives of human beings than all he accomplished for their comfort and convenience in transportation.

Literally no person, young or old, in the United States today lives untouched by the benefits of Mr. Kettering's inventive genius. He worked at a very practical level. But what he, or anyone else, accomplished he always considered

47

of secondary importance to the mental attitude that spurs a man to achievement. All his life he impressed upon young men who worked in his laboratories that a man's future is largely determined by what he himself determines to make it. "There is little we can imagine in our minds," he told them, "that we may not expect to do." In his vision, greater things always lay ahead than behind; and greater things could lie ahead of any young man who dared to work hard at a practical level to achieve the things his mind was able to visualize for him.

Nothing roused Mr. Kettering's fine scorn more than the assumption that we have reached nearly the end of things in invention, or an attitude that belittled the value of individual human effort even though we live in a society progressing largely through group effort. Illustrating this second attitude, one of his favorite stories was of the man who bought a house and lot in a neglected neighborhood and set out to make a flower garden out of a yard filled with weeds and rubbish. A year later a visitor remarked to him,

"That's a wonderful garden you and the Lord have made, Jim."

"Yes," said Jim thoughtfully, "but you should have seen it when the Lord had it by himself."

Mr. Kettering had plenty of experience with the need for individual effort himself—more than most men have. For, as a young man, he found himself burdened with the handicap of bad eyes that made it a toss-up for years as to whether or not he could use them enough to give himself an education.

He was born on a farm near Loudonville, Ohio, in 1876, into a hard-working farm family whose five children were going to have to make for themselves any higher educational advantages they were to have. He said, often, that he was the "dumbest kid" in arithmetic in the whole school, so progress did not come easily to him even then. He was a boy, though, who preferred to admit before the whole school that he was dumb rather than pretend to understand something he actually did not understand. Fortunately he had a good teacher who took the trouble to help him understand and, when it came to mechanical things, young "Chas," as his family called him, took them apart and studied them himself till he understood why and how they worked. Once he used some butter-and-egg money that had been set aside to buy him some new clothes to purchase a microscope so he could examine small things better. The first "real" money he ever earned—fourteen dollars for cutting a neighbor's wheat crop—went into a telephone bought from a mail order house. It was completely taken apart almost as soon as it arrived.

This type of inquiring mind, common enough to boys with a mechanical bent, took added effort from one with "Chas" Kettering's near-sighted eyes. He had to put on thick-lensed glasses as a schoolboy. Friends of those years recalled later how he stooped forward as he walked in order to watch carefully where he was stepping. Poor eyesight did not deter him, though, from keeping his mother's sewing machine in order or from using his microscope for private investigations of wheat and weeds and corn and goldenrod. The interest he developed in the life processes of plants was one which remained with him as long as he lived and about which he eventually dared to visualize a great achievement.

At fifteen he entered the Loudonville High School and for four years walked the three miles to and from it each day.

The following fall he got his first regular job teaching at the Bunker Hill School about five miles from Loudonville. Something important occurred that year. An X-ray machine, the recent invention of the German Roentgen, was exhibited in Loudonville, and Mr. Kettering dismissed school to take his pupils to see it. This progressive kind of education threatened to cost him his job because one of his school directors thought an X-ray machine had nothing to do with the processes of education. In the end, the threat to his position evaporated and young Mr. Kettering had taken advantage of an opportunity to see for the first time how electricity could be transformed in an airless tube into an energy that was radiant and vividly penetrating without the use of wires.

This experience whetted his desire to study science. So, with what he saved that winter, he went to nearby Wooster in the spring to study Greek which was required for entrance to Wooster College. At this point he began to experience the setbacks that taught him the beginnings of the philosophy he preached to young men later—that they may expect to do anything their minds truly imagine. But while his mind had imagined a college degree in science, his study of Greek brought on headaches so severe that his brother had to go to Wooster to help him get home. For weeks that summer he was unable to use his eyes at all.

The next fall he got another job teaching school in Mifflin, and here he spent the time not needed for teaching in performing experiments in electricity with the town's druggist who was also interested in science. They had a little room they used as a laboratory and were having a wonderful time of it when, after a few months, the old eye trouble returned. He had to resign from his teaching job and undergo another siege of intense suffering to which the threat of blindness was now added. Then he was better again, and in the fall he set out for Columbus with his ticket and thirty-five dollars to enter Ohio State University, which did not require Greek for the student who wanted to study science. He had decided to make a professor out of himself.

He was, it must be admitted, not a very up-to-the-minute-looking college boy when he entered Ohio State. Not only was he several years older than the average freshman—he was twenty-two—but he was a tall, stooped, lanky country boy with a shock of black hair who had never seen a street car until he reached Columbus. He found an inexpensive boarding house, matriculated in electrical engineering at O.S.U. and spent as much time as possible that winter in the college laboratories. He used twice as many chemicals as the other students—and students had to pay for their own chemicals—because he was rarely satisfied to do an experiment just as the textbook called for. He always wanted to see what would happen if he did something else, too.

It was an exciting winter so far as science was concerned. Then, with the spring, came the return of the headaches. A fellow student read aloud to him; he saved his eyes and passed his examinations. But he had scarcely gotten a start in his sophomore year's work when a sudden attack occurred of far greater severity, and it seemed for a while that he was very near to blindness. Big, strapping six-footer that he was, he had to give up and go home. The threat of blindness was seriously upon him and he began to train himself to use his hands to do many of the things for which he had once used his eyes and to develop his sense of touch to replace his sense of sight wherever possible as the blind must do. Even after he

was able to use his eyes again, he continued to train his hands
to obey his mind so that eventually he was not only able to
write with both hands at once, but to write different things
with each hand simultaneously.

It seemed obvious as his headaches lessened and his eyes
began to recover again that he should not return to his
studies. The doctor said, and Kettering himself knew, that
an outdoor job would probably be best for his health. So as
soon as he was physically able he found work with the Star
Telephone Company, helping to put up a new line at Ashland
a few miles north of Loudonville. By the end of the summer
he was foreman of the gang. That fall the Company asked
him if he could put in the Ashland exchange. Kettering said
yes and telegraphed to New York for that excellent textbook,
Kempster B. Miller's *American Telephone Practice.* Book
in hand, he went to work and put in the first central-battery
exchange in Ashland. Any intelligent fellow could have done
the job, he said later, if they just followed Miller's book carefully.

He was twenty-five before he was able to return to Ohio
State as a sophomore. But several years of outdoor work had
been effective in healing the inner mechanism that had given
way to cause his illnesses and now he went back to achieve
what his mind had imagined for him. Two years' experience
with the Star Telephone Company had given him, too, a
firm grasp of the practical values inherent in scientific progress and had made him impatient, as he remained throughout his life, with scientific research that does not have as its
aim some betterment in the lives of human beings. A telephone to him was not a scientific theory that sounded excellent in a textbook. It was a mechanism by which he could

enable two business men or two housewives in Ashland to talk to each other over a wire. If some mechanical difficulty arose to prevent easy talking, that seemed to Mr. Kettering a matter of first importance. Of what use is "pure science" in a laboratory, he would ask himself, if it does not bring practical constructive benefits to human beings?

This intense respect for practical results was doubtless a spur to help him achieve them. At any rate, he found no difficulty, back at Ohio State, in making good money from special jobs that soon began to find their way to him when a special kind of troubleshooter was needed in and about Columbus. He had the insight, too, to see how much a quick way out of trouble was worth in dollars and cents to an industry or a business man. If he could eliminate the difficulty successfully in less time than other people, why should his work not be worth more money? He asked for, and received, good pay when he accomplished knotty jobs quickly. For one night's work, during which he detected and corrected a failure in a telephone cable that was causing serious interruptions of service, he was offered more than the one hundred and twenty-five dollars he accepted.

His desire for practical results helped him know before long that he did not want to be a college professor. The more he saw of textbook and classroom science, the less he wanted to give his life to it. When, at nearly twenty-eight, he received his diploma, he had given up the idea entirely. He had an opportunity to remain at Ohio State, but accepted a position instead as an electrical inventor for the National Cash Register Company in Dayton.

The cash register, as it is known today, is sometimes said to do everything but talk. When Mr. Kettering went to Dayton in 1904 it was doing only a few of these things. At that time, for example, every time a sale was made the clerk had to ring it up by hand. This was an annoyance to the clerk, but it became much more than that to the machine. The irritation caused in a busy, often overtired person who had to go through the motion of turning the handle was so great that he would take it out on the cash register by giving the handle a much more vigorous wrench and turn than was necessary. This was so hard on the inner mechanism that machines got out of order, and this in turn caused irritation in the man who had bought it and must either get it repaired or buy a new cash register.

The ideal solution would be to have the clerk push a button or lever which would perform the handle-turning job for him. Extra wear and tear on the machine would be eliminated by having the operation regulated mechanically into as gentle and even a process as possible. The problem had been attacked many times, but all the solutions had necessitated a motor as big as the cash register itself. The job of finding a better solution was now put up to the new electrical inventor.

Within a year C.K., as he was now called, had made the electrically driven cash register possible. This was the first of his important inventions. With its success he began to learn a lesson that has often proved a sad one for the practical man—namely, that when a satisfactory product is made which does not wear out, resales of that product are lessened. People who used his improved cash register did not need to buy them as often as they had bought the old ones because they did not wear out nearly so fast.

Far from being discouraged, C.K. set out to make other

improvements on the machine. His idea was to keep on improving his product so that a person would not be satisfied too long with an old model because a new one had advantages that had not been possible with the older one. So the electrically-driven cash register began to do more and more new things, until a whole electrical-credit system for department stores came into existence with several kinds of electrically controlled accounting and auditing machines to supplement the machine on which he had first started to work. Far from making customers permanently satisfied, he kept them wanting the better products that made the best model of any given year outmoded a few years later.

While with the National Cash Register Company, Mr. Kettering began working at the problem of electric starters, an interest which was soon to take him into the larger field of the automobile. His first laboratory for individual work— the beginning of the world-famous Dayton Engineering Laboratories—was made possible through some $1500 Mrs. Kettering had saved out of his modest Cash Register salary. It was here that Mr. Kettering worked out the Delco System with which most Americans have long been familiar. This system for battery starting, lighting and ignition of automobiles was later developed into a system for farm lighting, too, and at their farm, his parents enjoyed one of the first installations, a gift from their son.

Mr. Kettering's practical sense now asserted itself again. He formed a partnership that could market these inventions to financial advantage, and others he knew would follow them. With Colonel Edgar A. Deeds, the National Cash Register executive who had hired him after his graduation from Ohio State, the Dayton Engineering Laboratory Company was formed. It laid the foundations for considerable financial success.

To tell the complete story of the Dayton laboratories would take a long book. Suffice it here to say that Mr. Kettering threw himself into problems there that gave such promise to the automobile industry that his laboratories were taken over by General Motors in 1919. A year later he became a vice president of that company and head of its research, a status he enjoyed until his retirement in 1947. As G.M.'s "Boss Kett" he had a big hand in developing Ethyl gasoline, Duco finish (in which the du Ponts, too, had a hand) crank-case ventilation and a two-cycle Diesel engine, to mention only a few of the numerous practical research projects he engaged in and saw through to a successful finish.

In this era of his life Mr. Kettering, who had started out as a more or less solitary worker, became the type of inventor whose work is largely the result of collaboration of effort on the part of many workers in big laboratories. As a director of research, he was responsible for the spending of many millions of dollars on projects which, in the long run, usually turned out to be profitable commercially. He was a great believer in that long run—that is, in the need for longer and heavier financing of new projects than many bankers and industrialists were willing to underwrite. He believed that research, properly conducted, with its results nursed along over longer periods of time (through the shirt-losing period, he used to call it) would open up vast new industries in this country that would solve our problem of unemployment. He put part of the blame for the depression of the 1930's publicly on the horse-and-buggy methods of financing research and new industries by unimaginative bankers and industrialists living in a motor age.

Whether or not Boss Kett's business philosophy was comprehensive enough, had it been properly applied, to solve the problems of unemployment and depression, as a scientific research man he spoke with authority. He insisted research was an attitude of mind, not just a piece of work necessitating a well-equipped laboratory for its fulfillment, because the attitude of mind is the bigger part of good research. Young men need an intelligently inquiring attitude toward whatever interests them, backed by the conviction that some day someone will be doing things that are now pronounced impossible. Another of his favorite stories was of how he told some of his men, as they were going off to a scientific meeting in a distant city, to talk with scientists there who were interested in a certain problem, to see if suggestions for its solution might be obtained. His men came back to tell him this particular problem could not be solved because—and then they enumerated the reasons they had been given to prove it was incapable of solution.

"That's great," he told them, "especially since we solved it while you were away."

This "it-can-be-done" attitude of his did not mean that he welcomed an unintelligently optimistic attitude. This was evidenced by the relish with which he used to tell the story of a couple of men who decided they would produce a universal solvent which would dissolve any substance at all. They sold the idea to financial backers who erected a laboratory for them and provided funds for research. One day a farmer came along, ambled into the laboratory and asked them what they were doing. They told him their idea—they were going to create the "Universal Solvent" which would dissolve every substance known to man.

"That's a great idea," said the farmer, "but, heck, what are you going to put it in?"

When asked what he visualized, specifically, as the new research and industries of the future, Mr. Kettering always replied that he did not like to be a prophet because no one could foresee accurately, even in a single business like the automobile business, what models would be like two years ahead. However, he predicted new trends in housing before many people in the construction industry had accepted them. He said many families would be no more willing to live in old-model homes than to drive old-model cars. His own home in Dayton, which he built in 1914, was probably the first air-conditioned home in America. With Diesel engine development making possible what it did for heating and ventilating units in small buildings, he claimed intelligent people would not long continue to be willing to pay coal bills necessitated in houses which put a window (a refrigerating unit) at one end of a room and a radiator (a heating unit) at the other. In cold weather this type of construction operates heating and refrigerating units in opposition to each other because of air leaks around the window. Then, on hot days, the refrigerating unit, open or closed with the sun beating upon it, becomes a heating unit! Much that he predicted about home building in the 1930's had come to pass before his death.

Long before his death he put his mark upon the future of what he considered the most important research problem facing scientists of his day. He established the C. F. Kettering Foundation for the Study of Chlorophyll and Photosynthesis, with a research laboratory at Antioch College. His boyhood interest in growing things had clung to him all through the years and he described the purpose of the research he wanted his money to foster in terms a child could understand. It was to help answer the question, "Why is grass green?" If that question could be answered it would give scientists a key to the problem that had long fascinated the imaginations of men—the problem of how to use the sun's energy directly as grass does, instead of having to let it rest in the earth for millions of years before it was usable as coal or oil.

In the years between his retirement at General Motors and his death in 1958, Mr. Kettering spent many happy hours in the Antioch laboratory. He lived long enough to see scientists begin to put solar energy to practical use and to know science was on its way toward revealing more and more of the secrets held in the growth of a single blade of grass.

FREDERICK G. COTTRELL

(1 8 7 7 – 1 9 4 8)

Founder of the Research Corporation, Whose Inventions Gave Us Cleaner Air and Salvaged Industrial Wastes

◆

PERHAPS YOU are familiar with the name Cottrell, perhaps not. But whether you are or not, you are bound to have been within range of some industrial plant equipped with an important apparatus that bears the Cottrell name. In more than thirty countries in the world today Cottrell Electrical Precipitators are busy taking the dust and contaminating smoke and fumes out of the gases eventually discharged into the air we have to breathe. And out of the valuable patents covering this precipitation process has grown the Research Corporation and its successful experiments in the handling of patent profits for the advancement of science rather than merely for individual gain. So any sketch of the life of Frederick Cottrell must be a picture both of him and of the Research Corporation he brought into existence.

It all began out in California in the early 1900's. Frederick

Cottrell had returned from Germany where a semester's study in Berlin had been followed by further work at the University of Leipzig which won for him a doctor's degree in science. Back in America, a position in the department of chemistry at his earlier alma mater, the University of California, was giving him access to a fairly good laboratory—every scientist's dream—a certain amount of freedom for research and a modest salary. But it so happened that this young Ph.D. had financial responsibilities heavier than could be met by his salary. So he was on the lookout for work that might supplement his income through profitable use of his spare time, especially in his summer vacations.

It seemed to young Dr. Cottrell that profitable economies in many growing young industries might be effected by recovery of some of the waste products that were escaping in the smokestacks increasingly dotting the western landscape. He was familiar with the principle of electrical precipitation of particles suspended in smoke as established by Sir Oliver Lodge and other workers in the 1880's. Work in this field had been dropped because it could not then be developed on a scale large enough to be of commercial value. Dr. Cottrell believed the time had come when this work might be carried into its next stage because the science of electricity had advanced to the place where a current of sufficiently high voltage could be produced to make large-scale operation possible.

With the possibility of high voltage equipment that had not been available to his predecessors, and ideas of his own on how he could carry their work further with it, he set his own peculiar genius to work on the problem of removing waste from smoke in smokestacks. In time, with valuable new steps in the process ready for patenting and with financial aid from several friends, a small unit was designed for sulphuric acid waste recovery, and permission was received to install it in the du Pont de Nemours sulphuric acid plant at Pinole, on San Francisco Bay, to demonstrate its commercial possibilities. It was the intention of the group backing Dr. Cottrell to sell the du Pont Company the idea of taking out a license on the new process—if the small unit was successful—and having a larger unit installed, simply because it could more than pay for itself in the economies effected.

It so happened that at nearby Vallejo Junction, the Selby Lead and Smelting Company was in serious difficulties due to damage suits, filed but not settled, because of destruction wrought on surrounding territory through fumes escaping from the smokestacks of their plant. When the demonstration at Pinole showed practical possibilities, the Selby people set about to sell Dr. Cottrell the idea that they were better prospective clients than the du Ponts because their problem involved nuisance elimination as well as operating economy. The result was that for several years the Pinole proposition was dropped and Dr. Cottrell's time was well taken up with new problems at the Selby plant.

The installation at their smelter at Vallejo Junction in 1907—the first Cottrell installation on a commercial scale—was highly successful. And it was a blessing for industrialists that a new process was becoming available to point a way out of their troubles. A storm of protest against the destruction caused by escaping gases with their sometimes poisonous dust and fumes had been smouldering for years throughout the West, and damage suits had been brought long before the Selby unit had been installed. These suits were growing in numbers as offending companies paid damages in their attempts to ward off the possibility of injunctions that would force them to discontinue certain operations.

The Anaconda Copper Company, for example, found itself the defendant in a suit that was called the "three-million-dollar damage suit" before it dragged to its end in the United States Supreme Court many years later. The United States Government lost thousands of acres of fine timber land. Ranch owners brought suits because their cattle died from arsenic poisoning traced to arsenic deposited on grazing land from the smoke and fumes of a nearby smelter. Cement-manufacturing companies were being sued by municipalities because of tons of dust deposited on them daily. One such cement company at Riverside, California, was being sued by owners of ruined orange groves whose acres were valued at as much as $4000 each. All in all, industrial plant owners had an expensive problem on their hands, and once it became known what a Cottrell precipitator would do, people felt justified in pressing suits to their limit.

Dr. Cottrell continued his teaching at the University of California while his first precipitators were proving themselves and business men, with their practical operating experts, were literally wearing a path to his doorstep in the hope of finding ways out of their difficulties. Each plant presented problems of its own, and even though some business and industrial leaders were laughing loudly at the idea of "calling in the professors when it's a good practical head that is needed," others were smart enough to see that this particular professor's head was what was needed to solve these particular practical problems. In fact, Frederick Cottrell is an excellent example of the college professor who pulled some of industry's chestnuts out of the fire when practical men at the plants were failing, and his electrical precipitators soon began to be a part of many plants' equipment.

The story of the success of the Cottrell Process all over the world would fill books. But all those books would stack up to a mere nothing beside the freight trains that could be filled with the ash and dust and valuable solids and liquids that have been removed, through the application of Cottrell's patents, from the smoke and gases in industry's belching, billowing smokestacks. Smoke still makes many of our cities dirty. But wherever a "Cottrell" has been installed, it is taking from 90 to 98 per cent (with special apparatus actually up to 99.99 per cent) of all particles, no matter how small, out of escaping smoke and gases. That is the advantage of the electrical method over filters and other processes for smokestack collection. The electrical method works on *all* particles regardless of their minute size, and regardless, too, of their temperature and whether they are solid or liquid.

Dr. Cottrell eventually used currents up to 100,000 volts and over to create a strong electrostatic field in the flues leading to the smokestack from which the smoke and fumes from an industrial process must be discharged. Physical changes take place here, both in the molecules of gas and in the tiny solids that are held in suspension. The result is an approximately 99 per cent clean gas escaping at the top, while the particles that would have been dirt and impurities in the outside air are forced downward through a hopper to be collected in the basement.

In the beginning, Cottrell precipitators were used merely to eliminate the nuisance of dirty smoke and obnoxious fumes. But that was soon to become the lesser reason in persuading the owner of an industry to undertake the rather considerable expense of the installation. Out of the dirt and ash in the basement, valuable materials began to be retrieved. A survey made some twenty years after the first installation showed that, on the North American continent alone, upwards of ten million dollars worth of industrial wastes was being saved each year. And many more plants have been equipped since then. Thus, the equipment, costly though it is, often pays for itself in a comparatively short time, and in many cases it is put in purely for the value of the material to be recovered. To illustrate:

As early as 1940 one single metal-mining installation saved a million dollars yearly through the recovery of valuable materials, to say nothing of the smoke-and-fume nuisance abatement. Another precipitator—this one in a paper mill—reported a saving of six tons of soda salts in one *day's* operation. Other savings being achieved at individual plants daily included: ten tons of arsenic, four and a half tons of alumina, 5500 pounds of concentrated sulphuric acid, 208 tons of 12 per cent copper dust, and fifty-five tons of 20 per cent copper dust.

The elimination of dirt alone, however, is a powerful feature in the value of precipitators, especially for big cities. Without a good one, a big power plant such as the Hell Gate plant in New York City could throw out as much as a thousand tons of fine dust and ash in a day's operation. Think, then, what all the plants in a city like New York could discharge in terms of dirt alone! The Riverside (California) Portland Cement Company, which installed one of the earliest of Dr. Cottrell's precipitators in 1912, collected well over a million tons of cement dust in less than thirty years, or enough fully to load a freight train more than two hundred miles long! Moreover, the company profited from the potash recovered as well as from the cement dust. It was sold as valuable fertilizer for the very orange groves once threatened with destruction from cement dust.

More impressive, though, than the technical accomplishments of Dr. Cottrell's precipitators is the story of what he did with the valuable patents which gave him exclusive rights on the use of his invention. That is where the Research Corporation, mentioned in the first paragraph of this story, has its part.

To begin with, bear in mind that getting a big new industrial operation perfected for patenting was not a summer holiday's work. It took years of brain work and hand and foot work in laboratory and plants—work that Frederick Cottrell had to do in addition to his regular teaching at the University. But the time came when his invention was admittedly a success, with the possibility of becoming a money-maker on a large scale. The question then was what to do with the patents. He might sell them and make a tidy sum immediately. Or he might give up a life he had intended to devote to scientific research and go into the business of exploiting his patents and make for himself—more slowly—part of the many millions of dollars the patents would eventually save for industry. These seemed to be the alternatives.

But he did neither of these things. He began, instead, to hunt around for some scientific institution or organization to which he could give his patents with the stipulation that a good part of the profits were to be used for the advancement of science.

Do not get the idea that this scientist-inventor was somewhat of a fool about money. He had a very practical mind about money and had every intention of taking care of himself rightfully with this work he had labored so long to accomplish. Also, there were several friends who had backed him financially when he had to have money to continue his experimental work. He wanted his patents to take care of them similarly, too. But—and this is where he was different—he had his own ideas about what "rightfully" meant.

At this point in Frederick Cottrell's life we have the usual picture of the "poor but worthy young man" quite in reverse. Instead of a poor young scientist trying to find money to be able to continue his work, we find this far from prosperous young scientist trying to find some institution to which he could give his patents so that they might some day help other scientists to continue their work. He hunted in vain, because no existing organization felt it was equipped to do the kind of work necessary in handling patents successfully.

The Smithsonian Institution, however, was interested and willing to help him where it could. Together they worked out a plan to establish the type of organization that was needed for the acceptance of gifts of this nature. Quite possibly, Smithsonian officials remembered how their former secretary, Samuel P. Langley, had refused to patent his inventions because he could not bring himself to commercialize what science had revealed to him, only to have his inventions commercialized by others. At any rate, through the joint efforts of the Smithsonian Institution and Dr. Cottrell, the Research Corporation came into existence in 1912 for the purpose of earning funds to be used for the advancement of science.

This was a brand new idea. Funds of many millions of dollars had already been set aside by men of wealth for scientific purposes. They were based on endowments of money whose income was to be used. To give such huge sums was the privilege of rich men alone. But with Dr. Cottrell, we find a man without wealth establishing the financial underpinnings of an organization that, through its earnings instead of income from money already earned, would eventually contribute millions of dollars to dozens of scientific organizations so that work—often the cherished work of some young scientist who would gladly finance it himself if he could—might continue.

One idea basic to the Research Corporation's purpose was that brain power, if properly used for the advantage of all, is the most valuable resource a nation has, greater by far than its coal, oil or gold. And using brain power to best advantage, in Dr. Cottrell's mind certainly included giving the people who had been instrumental in helping him with his work in precipitation their rightful share of the profits. So, in presenting his patents to the Research Corporation, he specified that the rights in a few of the western states where the patents were already of value were to remain the property of the company organized by the group that had backed the work. That was how this group was to be rightfully taken care of. In other words, they were assured the right to earn money from the patents by establishing a business and earning that return from day to day. The Western Precipitation Company, as this company was called, had a long record of work well done, dividends well paid.

But the Research Corporation to which all other rights were transferred, pays no dividends. That is written into its charter. The men who originally put up some $10,000 to get the work started were repaid three years later out of the first earnings. The stock that had been issued to them was turned back into the Corporation. Also written into its charter is the privilege of accepting gifts of patents or patentable ideas from other scientists or inventors. Over the years, the organization has been very careful about what it accepts because it is a commercial concern that operates for profits. It grants money aid to science with no idea of profit for itself. But the idea back of its acceptance of patents and other gifts is to earn funds—not just handle them—to be used for the advancement of science, so it may not sink money in foolish or trivial inventions. In accepting a gift it thinks is going to be a good business proposition, the Corporation makes an arrangement with the donor which he—or, in some cases, she—desires as "rightful" compensation, or it will accept the gift outright if the donor so desires.

Possibly an explanation of just how the Research Corporation functions with a gift will make the plan clearer. Take the original Cottrell patents as an example. Within its territory the organization functioned as would any other engineering or contracting concern. When a copper smelter wished to use the process, the Corporation licensed it and sent its own staff to design, build and make test runs of the equipment. One difficulty in handling patents is that improvements and alternatives are continually necessary as industry progresses so the Corporation soon found licensing and collecting royalties would be the smaller part of its job if it was to maintain its place in American industry. Like any other similar successful corporation, it had to develop its own design, construction and service departments and adopt business policies that permitted it to survive in a competitive industrial system.

Each new patent gift its Board subsequently accepted offered individual problems. The early years were difficult years as they are likely to be with any corporation. In spite of the fact that the electrical precipitation patents were a spectacular success, the original Cottrell patents expired before the Research Corporation had any significant sums of money available for use elsewhere to further scientific research. But by this time, further precipitation patents along with others in related fields had come into its possession, and it had established its own capacity to deliver the goods. Its success was assured.

So much for the Research Corporation and how it functions. But to tell how this Corporation functions is an easier task than to answer the question: "What made a man like Dr. Cottrell bring it into existence?" When the question was put to him, as it sometimes was, he always strove to avoid being thought visionary or "foolishly" unselfish. He pointed out that his own share from the patents was satisfactory and that truly brilliant inventors had often failed to achieve this when they tried to commercialize their patents.

"But you aren't even a modestly rich man," one of his questioners reminded him.

"That wasn't necessary, or perhaps even desirable," was the answer. "I wanted to enjoy my life and that meant being free to continue scientific work rather than being tied to one phase of it primarily to make money—and then probably to worry about how best to use it without losing it."

He admitted he would like to see scientific achievement used less for enriching a comparatively few people and more for enriching the well-being of mankind by a better distribution of the things money can buy. He thought men's minds had capacity for creating an economic system that could handle the achievements of twentieth-century science better than he saw them being handled. He did his bit in this direction. His faith was heightened when some other scientists took advantage of the Research Corporation's idea and turned patents over to them.

Throughout his life Dr. Cottrell did primarily what he wanted to do. He left teaching to go into government service in 1911, eventually moving to Washington where he lived until 1944. He was Chief Chemist, then Chief Metallurgist, and finally Director of the Bureau of Mines, in these capacities playing an important part in developing helium gas for airships during the first World War, and then going to Europe during the Peace Conference as one of our government's technical experts. Later he became Chief of the Division of Fertilizers and Fixed Nitrogen Investigations for the Department of Agriculture. He was an authority on the chemistry of nitrogen fixation and the manufacture of mineral fertilizers, advising Congress on the technical aspects of Muscle Shoals between the close of World War I and the creation of the Tennessee Valley Authority. He served as chief consulting chemist through the early critical months of TVA's organization.

Dr. Cottrell's mind was so fertile it is impossible, in a few pages, to mention all phases of his work. Scientific societies honored him with medals and awards, including the Holley Medal and the Washington Award. Important though his technical and scientific work was, though, it was his unusual outlook on life that made him somewhat unique among men. To have the best in life meant, to him, to have the privilege of doing well the work he preferred while giving to his family what was needed for a good—not a lavish—life. Beyond those needs, he preferred to share all else in such a way that others might be enabled to do their best work, too, as they assumed financial responsibilities for their families.

After leaving Washington he returned to California. He lived near the University where he had both studied and taught, and died in its halls one morning in November, 1948, while attending a meeting of the National Academy of Sciences of which he was a member.

ROBERT R. WILLIAMS

(1886–   )

Whose Work in Isolating and then Synthesizing Vitamin B₁ Helped Make Better Health Standards Possible

◈

R OBERT R. WILLIAMS is a man who might be described as having led a double life in science. In each he was highly successful. In the first, he followed the logical steps to success. With a bachelor's and then a master's degree in chemistry, he rose step by step until, as he approched his fortieth birthday, he became Chemical Director of the Bell Telephone Laboratories in New York City. This was a challenging and highly responsible position, and he remained in it till he had attained the age when most men are looking forward to retirement in a few years. This life, in itself, has all the requirements for a success story.

But Dr. Williams has been leading, simultaneously, a second and quite separate life in chemistry. In spare time left over from his demanding work at the Bell laboratories, he kept investigating substances derived from grain which contained something that restored health to human beings suffering from a type of illness which could cause death if it were not administered. The "something" was proving very elusive to chemists trying to learn more about it. Search for it became Williams' avocation. For twenty-five years, in an era when claims were being made that valuable scientific contributions could be achieved only in big and expensively equipped laboratories, he pursued his search until he had isolated the substance we know as vitamin B_1—or thiamin chloride—and discovered its chemical structure. Much of that work was done in his wife's washtubs and the family garage. The results were so valuable in terms of money as well as health that the success of his avocational interest is the greater part of his life achievement.

The background of Dr. Williams' early life had a distinct bearing upon the problem that caught his interest and earned the millions of dollars that he made available to other scientists in pursuit of their researches. Born in a missionary family in India in 1886, Robert was brought to America by his parents as a young boy after his father had been crippled in an accident which unfitted him for further work as a missionary. Life was none too easy for the Williams' children during their school days in Kansas and California, for the accident had handicapped their father severely for any kind of work at all. Robert earned his living at an earlier age than most American boys of his generation. The new suit of clothes given him by his parents on his thirteenth birthday was the last gift that cost money, other than the privilege of living at home, his parents were ever able to afford. He earned his way through high school and through Ottawa University near his home in Kansas by any kind of early-rising, strong-arm work available. Then he left for the University of Chicago to earn his bachelor's and master's degrees which he received in 1907 and 1908.

It would seem that a man who was to find chemistry both his vocation and avocation during a long work life might have recognized his interest in the subject at least as early as in his high school days. In Robert Williams' case this did not happen. Actually, it was his mother who first suggested a career in chemistry, but not until after he had finished high school. Part of the reason for her suggestion was the fact that they happened to know about a correspondence course in the subject that did not cost much. So, though he had decided to major in chemistry in college, it was not until he was in the midst of work for his master's degree that he felt sure he had chosen wisely to specialize in this subject.

Even with two degrees in chemistry in his pocket, it seemed he might not go on with it. Although an attractive position at Dalhousie University in Halifax was offered him, Mr. Williams made a decision to accept, instead, a position as a teacher in the elementary schools in the Philippine Islands. He took the precaution of qualifying, by a supplementary examination, as a chemist for the United States Civil Service, too, but as he left for the Orient in which he had spent part of his youth he realized that he might never use his science major. He believed our country had a responsibility to the Filipinos and that free education, for all who would accept it, was a foundation stone for the discharge of this responsibility that would enable this native people to develop into free and responsible citizens.

Shortly after his arrival in the Philippines in 1908, he was transferred to the Bureau of Science in Manila and presented with a problem. Dr. Vedder of the U.S. Army Medical Corps handed him a bottle of liquid syrup made from rice polishings—that is, made from the bran and germ which had been removed and discarded in the process of making natural rice into the polished white rice with which all Americans are familiar.

"There is something in this syrup that cures beriberi in babies," said Dr. Vedder. "Find out what it is and see if you can make it in the laboratory."

It took Robert Williams twenty-five years to fill that order, but he filled it.

When he took that bottle of health-restoring liquid in his hands he was already familiar with the stories of how certain doctors had come to believe there was a life-saving substance in rice polishings. He had heard the tale, for instance, of how, when the United States had bought the Philippine Islands at the end of the Spanish-American War, they had decided to give prisoners in Manila jails "better" food than the Spaniards had been giving them and to install American sanitary measures to keep down the spread of disease. One idea of "better" food in those days had included the substitution of polished white rice for the supposedly inferior native brown rice with which the prisoners had been supplied. When beriberi spread rapidly after this substitution had been made, the Americans promptly cleaned and scoured the prisons, thinking that beriberi was a disease spread by filth and contact with the sick, just as they were thinking yellow fever was a filth disease in Cuba.

Beriberi had continued to spread, regardless of sanitary measures. Then American doctors had taken heed of the work of a Dutch physician, Dr. Christian Eijkman in Java, who had published a report telling that he was able to produce beriberi symptoms in chickens by feeding them white rice instead of brown, and then cure them by giving them an extract from the rice polishings. So by the time Robert Williams had arrived in the Philippines, American doctors in Manila had not only put the brown rice back on the prison menu, but they were able to cure infantile beriberi with this same kind of extract.

Mr. Williams began his search for the elusive substance in the syrup from rice polishings by making use of chickens as experimental animals. Step by step he refined the syrup, and at each step, provided he had not removed the substance he was hunting, a smaller dose of the remaining syrup was effective in preventing beriberi in the chickens. The smaller the effective dose became, the nearer he knew he was to isolating what he searched for in its pure form.

Most doctors, however, still refused to admit that the disease they could cause in chickens and the human disease were actually the same as Dr. Eijkman believed. It was therefore necessary for Williams to confirm his progress by trying his extracts on human beings. He undertook the duty of preparing rice-polish extract for distribution in free health clinics in the poorer districts of Manila, especially for babies who had developed beriberi while nursing at their mothers' breasts. He cultivated an acquaintance with the doctors who attended the poor and enlisted their services. He was not a medical man himself, so he depended for his confirmatory experiments on cases that had been officially reported as beriberi.

Sometimes he insisted on dosing the babies himself because it looked to him as if mothers often got more of his precious liquid on the outside than on the inside of the babies. He learned to recognize the stage of the disease which means death is only a few hours off—a period of weird, almost sound-less crying, of breath coming in gasps, of a wild pulse and blue lips. In cases which had reached this stage, the young chemist would administer the dose himself and sit down on the split-bamboo floor of the shack with the mother to watch results. In as short a time as three hours, the baby's weird cry-ing would cease—but not in death. Instead, its breathing would become regular, its pulse quiet, its lips would begin to lose their bluish cast—*all as a result of something in the germ and bran of rice*. Then the child would nurse hungrily from its mother's breast and drop off into a peaceful sleep.

After many a day's or night's experience like this, Williams would go back to his laboratory to hunt for the substance re-sponsible for the miracle. What a blessing to the Orient it would be if he could but find it! For five years his work con-tinued. Although he helped cure beriberi, he did not find the specific substance responsible for the cure. And then, be-cause of changes in the work of the Bureau of Science, he was transferred from the Philippines to the Bureau of Chemistry in Washington to continue his work on this substance to which the name "vitamin" had been given.

By this time other vitamins in addition to the anti-beriberi curative were thought to exist. But this earliest known vita-min was to be much more difficult than some of the others to isolate because—as was not known until many more years of work had been accomplished by many scientists in a number of different countries—vitamin B was not one but a whole family of vitamins. For this reason it kept leading scientists up many a blind alley, depending on which animal was chosen for observation or which symptom was selected as the criterion of progress.

After less than two years' work in Washington, Williams' vitamin experiments were brought to an end by the entry of the United States into World War I. He was transferred to war service and, from that time on, his study of vitamins was to be only an avocation relegated to spare time and continued under trying conditions. After the war he left Civil Service for work in private industry and fitted up his own laboratory in his garage. He stretched his modest salary past the needs of a family including four growing children to finance his research as best he could. But through thick and thin he stuck to his self-appointed task of seeking in rice polishings the unknown substance that he had seen perform miracles in Manila.

The first ten years following his return to America passed. In 1926 two Dutch doctors, Jansen and Donath, announced that they had succeeded in isolating the anti-beriberi substance in its pure form. This was a big step forward but the amounts the Dutch doctors were able to obtain by the process they had worked out were so small that its purity was doubtful (in time it was proved to be only "nearly pure") and the chemical study which could determine its structure was greatly handicapped. So Williams worked on, devising his own processes, failing, getting new material and starting all over again. At five o'clock, with a good day's work back of him, he would leave for home and put in most of the hours till midnight or later on his vitamin research. When the work outgrew the garage, an old New York Hospital room was made available. Later, laboratory space and quarters for his experimental animals were provided at Columbia University. When the expenses outgrew the personal financing he was able to provide through private economies, money gifts were obtained. The Carnegie Corporation came to the rescue when the demands for heavier financing increased during the latter years of work, providing him with helpers.

Six years after the two Dutch doctors had succeeded in isolating the particular B vitamin they were hunting, Williams succeeded in getting, by use of his own chemical process, the pure crystals he had been after for more than twenty years. Of great importance was the fact that his process gave him the crystals in greater quantity than Jansen and Donath had been able to get. The amount of crystals needed for successful chemical analysis had an important bearing on this part of the work, and the scale of operations necessary in the Williams' process indicates why he eventually outgrew his garage laboratory and personal financing. In their first stage, his experiments required a 1300 gallon tank. In their last stage, they were reduced to a diminutive test tube. In the water-soaked rice polish in the tank, forty to fifty parts of the vitamin were present in every million parts of the rice polish, but only about one-fourth of it could be recovered as crystalline material. That was approximately ten parts of the vitamin recovered for every million parts of rice polish. Although they were far more precious than gold to Williams when he got them, some of the very earliest crystals—several hundred milligrams of them—were sent back to Manila so they could be put to immediate practical trial.

Once Williams and his co-workers had sizable quantities of the crystals available, it took them less than three years to determine their molecular structure. When their structure was known, the laboratory manufacture of the vitamin in synthetic form was a matter of only a few months.

But would the synthetic, laboratory-made crystals perform the miracle? That was the question now! Had the scientist linked together nitrogen, hydrogen, carbon, oxygen, sulphur and chlorine in the laboratory in exactly the right way so that a few white specks of it would perform the miracle of the syrup made from the germ and bran of rice or by the little natural crystals it had taken so many tons of material to produce? Williams thought he had linked the various elements accurately, but he had been disappointed many times before. The intricate patterns of the chemical structure of a so-called simple molecule offer many chances of going astray in the laboratory synthesis of a vitamin.

Robert Williams saw to it that he always had on hand groups of white rats in various stages of beriberi when each trial synthesis was completed. The proof of each synthetic product depended on what it did to the rats. That final trial of the first synthetically made vitamin B_1 on those sick "little brothers of mankind" was the most tense and dramatic moment of a whole quarter century of work. This time Williams felt confident, for so many other possibilities had been gradually eliminated. The result of the experiment is epitomized in the telegram he sent young Robert Waterman, who had been an ardent volunteer worker in the cause and later became his son-in-law:

THE RATS SAY YES

That brief sentence foretold miracles for America as well as for the Orient. As is well recognized today, long before the rats said yes and vitamin B_1 could be produced in laboratories in synthetic form, many so-called "well-fed" Americans were suffering from lack of this vitamin. They were not sick as were beriberi sufferers in the Orient. Beriberi is a most severe form of neuritis. Americans suffered from less severe forms of this disease. This was proved in many cases of illnesses that were helped by dosage with the new vitamin product as soon as doctors were able to give it to their patients.

Nor were Americans sick because of the effects of white rice in their diets. Wheat is our main cereal but, in turning away from whole wheat to become a nation of white-flour eaters, we had deprived ourselves of most of the B group of vitamins exactly as had Asiatics who became white-rice eaters several decades later. In one important way though, Americans had an advantage. Our population could afford to eat a wider variety of foods than could most Asiatics. Other foods were supplying us with enough B_1 to keep the lesser deficiency caused by its removal from our wheat flour from afflicting us with the severe results that accompany a more complete deficiency.

By the time medical men were verifying the beneficial results of the Williams' product on sick people all over our country, vitamin research had gone far enough for him and other scientists to know that the wider variety of foods Americans were eating were supplying only a fraction of some of the valuable B vitamins every healthy body needs which were—and still are—milled out of our wheat. Nature, often a lavish provider, is stingy with this family of vitamins. She provides them in an abundance sufficient for human needs mainly in the germs of cereal grains. As research continued, it became known that a percentage of Americans of all age groups suffered as a result of the removal of essential nutri-

ents from our wheat. Deficiency of B_1, for example, inter-
fered with normal growth and development of the young; it
was as essential for teen-agers as for older people. In short,
the absence of what we were discarding from our wheat to
feed to hogs and other farm animals had as ill effect on our
children as its presence had an excellent effect on the pigs!

As one way of lessening the health handicap caused by the
use of white flour Dr. Williams and others interested in national health problems began to urge the enrichment of this
impoverished flour by the addition of B_1. Before this step
could be taken, of course, B_1 would have to be available at
reasonable cost and in massive supply. Dr. Williams had
asked the Research Corporation, which Frederick Cottrell
had established for just such purposes, to handle the Williams-Waterman patents, and in a short time the Corporation
had licensed a number of pharmaceutical firms to use them.
The result was that synthetic B_1, or thiamin chloride, quickly
became available to millers at a reasonable cost. Five years
after the rats had said yes Dr. Williams had the satisfaction of
seeing the addition of B_1 to white flour on a nation-wide
scale.

This was the beginning of the enrichment program which
now gives us our white flour with a number of vitamins and
minerals added to it. True, enriched flour today restores only
a small fraction of the nutritious elements milled out of our
wheat—(there are fifteen or more B vitamins alone in wheat
germ!) but it is a better product than white flour without
those additions and a factor in giving children who use it
better opportunity for building healthy bodies during their
period of growth and keeping older people less subject to
some forms of illness in later life.

But that is only a part of the success story of Robert Williams' second life in science. When he put his patents into the hands of the Research Corporation their income, except for a share assigned to him and those who helped him in the work that made them possible, was also put into the hands of the Corporation, to be used for furthering nutritional research and supporting other work whose aim was to improve human nutrition. It soon became apparent that the Corporation's income from the patents would run into millions of dollars and, as he approched sixty, Dr. Williams left the Bell laboratories to become Director of Grants for the Research Corporation. It must have been one of his most satisfying duties to direct the vast sums coming, throughout the period covered by patent protection, from the pharmaceutical companies using the Williams' process. No attempt was made to build the Williams-Waterman Fund into a fund to exist permanently, after the expiration of the patents. Instead, most of the money was to be spent each year as the patents earned it.

Under Dr. Williams' personal direction, the Fund has fostered research and supported nutritional programs all over the world, geared to the food problems of the people in the countries receiving money grants. For example, programs were instituted that enriched cornmeal in our southern states and rice in the Philippines and Formosa. Cereal-enrichment programs were supported in Yugoslavia and Cuba. In India, Pakistan, Guatemala, Brazil and Chile grants were made to provide training to scientists of these countries that would help them solve nutritional problems existing in their midst. Other grants were given for work in Africa, while many have gone to colleges and universities here and abroad for the study of problems in human nutrition. Medical students from foreign lands have had the opportunity for study in American nutrition research centers, while our own students have been given the opportunity for field and laboratory research in foreign countries.

Dr. Williams has had high recognition from his peers for the valuable contributions he has made as a scientist and as a human being. He has been a member of the National Academy of Sciences since 1945 and is the recipient of a number of medals, including the Gibbs Medal of the American Chemical Society, the Cresson Medal, the Perkin Medal, the Chandler Medal and the Scott Medal of the City of Philadelphia.

EMIL TRUOG

(1884–   )

Pioneer in the Study of Soil Chemistry Who Devised
the First Accurate Practical Test to Measure Soil Acidity

◈

Emil truog intended to be a farmer. Instead, he became a professor of soils and, along with his work in teaching
young soil scientists, one of America's outstanding authorities
in the chemistry of soils. He was a pioneer in the development of soil-testing methods to determine lime and fertilizer
needs and in ways of applying fertilizers to keep soils healthily
able to release their life-building nutrients to the plants cultivated in them. Without this type of science our country
could not long grow the food essential to the health of its
rapidly expanding population.

Young Truog began to see some of the disheartening results of poor farming methods on the grain and livestock
farm in Wisconsin where he had been born in 1884. His
father and older brothers had cleared and put under the plow
most of its 230 acres and, even though these acres had so recently been cleared, some of them were showing signs of less-

ening fertility in Emil's early youth. He had the type of mind that was interested in family discussions about what ought to be tried next on certain fields where productivity was diminishing, and he studied the farm journals that discussed such problems. In fact, he found some of the semi-scientific articles in his father's farm journals more interesting than anything in his *Youth's Companion*.

For many months out of every year, life on the farm was too hard to allow much time for reading. Wisconsin winters found this youngest of the ten Truog children bucking two and three foot snowdrifts in a nipping temperature of twenty degrees below zero on his two and a half mile walk to and from school, and hustling with home chores both morning and evening. During reaping and threshing seasons he often rose before daylight, worked out of doors till dark, then helped feed the livestock and finish the milking. On such nights, summer and winter alike, there was little desire to read. All Emil wanted was to fall into bed, where he was asleep the minute his head hit the pillow.

But it was not all hard work in his boyhood. Between periods of constant work, there were others when he not only read, but fished and hunted, played ball and horseshoes, and tramped the woods where he came to know well the spots in which wild plums, cherries, currants and gooseberries grew. It was a happy life. It offered a happy future, and Emil wanted to continue it. He was going to be a farmer, and he was going to be the most intelligent kind of farmer he could.

At that period of his life, being an intelligent farmer did not mean much book learning to Emil Truog. Without the urging of a grade school teacher who recognized the promise of this student's inquiring mind, he might never have gone on to the four-year high school at Arcadia which was eight, rather than a mere two and one half miles, from his home. And again, though the study of physics and chemistry appealed strongly to him, he might not have wanted to go to college without the urging of a high school teacher who thought he should study further at the University of Wisconsin. Throughout his whole adolescence, farming exerted the strongest pull on Emil Truog, and to be a good farmer did not at first seem to him to necessitate a college education. It meant following in the footsteps of his Swiss immigrant parents who had inculcated in him a love of the land, a respect for hard work, and their philosophy that "all work should be done real well even if it takes all summer."

By the time their youngest son had his high school diploma the elder Mr. Truog, watching his fields grow less productive and unable to find ways to bring their yields back to what they had been, had begun to say it ought to be a good thing for the farm if Emil took the short course in agriculture offered by the State University. True to his home training of doing things "real well," Emil decided that if he went to college to study agriculture he wanted more than an abbreviated course. He would work for a bachelor's degree. The trouble was that the family finances were unable to provide him with money for this education. He worked and saved and at twenty-one was able to enter the University of Wisconsin's College of Agriculture. With some financial help from a sister and his own physical and mental efforts, he had his B.S. in Agriculture four years later.

Early in his college days, chemistry, especially as it pertained to agriculture, caught and held his imagination. And now, for the third time, it was his teachers who recognized

his abilities and urged him to continue. A research assistantship in the University's Department of Soils was made available to him. This enabled him to do graduate work and to
begin to pay back the money he had borrowed from his sister.
That was in 1909. He remained on the active staff of the Agricultural College of the University until his retirement as
Emeritus Professor in 1954—as Professor of Soils beginning in
1921. In the more than three decades of his full professorship,
the University of Wisconsin attracted more graduate students
in soils than any other university in the country, many of
them from foreign lands who took their learning and inspiration to their homelands to use in the underdeveloped areas
there.

The problem of soil acidity was one of the first to catch
Mr. Truog's imagination—and no wonder! This is one of the
problems in soil chemistry that has troubled tillers of the soil
from the days of antiquity. Without scientific knowledge,
rule-of-thumb practices had developed. Rotation of crops, for
example, was common among the old Greeks and Romans.
They fertilized soils with animal manures, scattered ashes
and sometimes even lime over their lands. And like the cook
who puts in a little of this and a little of that, stirs it up, puts
it in the oven and produces a lip-smacking cake, farmers all
the way down from antiquity sometimes had successful results from their rule-of-thumb practices in agriculture.

But the science of soil chemistry, the science which identi-
fies the specific soil conditions that cause crop failures before
it prescribes the proper treatment—much as physicians identify an illness before prescribing medication—did not exist until modern times. Thousands of years after the old Greeks and
Romans, George Washington and Thomas Jefferson, two of

the most intelligent farmers of their day, were practicing crop rotations and fertilizing with animal manures, much as had the farmers of antiquity. They fertilized fields with mud from creeks and marshes and went to great expense in procuring special seeds to grow, on ailing lands, the crops believed to be an essential part of intelligent crop rotation. Yet they left much of the land at Mount Vernon and Monticello in a run-down condition for those who followed. Some of their soils had suffered from one deficiency while others suffered from another deficiency, and no scientific way existed to differentiate between the "illnesses," so each soil could be treated properly for what was wrong with it.

Knowledge along these lines had increased somewhat by the nineteenth century. When Emil Truog was a boy on his father's farm he read in farm journals about soil acidity, that it was often the cause of crop failures and that it could be detected by means of a litmus paper test. In its simplest form the test consisted merely of cutting a slit in a lump of moist earth with a knife blade, inserting one end of a strip of blue litmus paper in the slit and pressing the soil against it. If, at the end of five minutes, the paper was pink, the test indicated an acid soil. If the soil was treated with lime, the acidity would be corrected so that clover or alfalfa or some other legume would grow on it again. Science, in Truog's boyhood, had gone far enough to know not only that a crop of legumes would be effective in increasing crop production the following year, but also *why* it did so. Legumes returned nitrogen to the soil and nitrogen was a very essential plant constituent.

This knowledge was good so far as it went, but the litmus paper test, Truog knew, was unsatisfactory because it did not go far enough. One of its weak points was that slight acidity often failed to show up. A more serious objection was that carbonic acid, a harmless acid given off in large quantities by living plant roots, turns blue litmus paper red, and there was no way of knowing whether the red color was the result of this harmlesss acid or of the actual acid causing soil acidity. The most serious objection, however, was that the test gave no definite indication of the degree of acidity and hence of whether one ton or five tons of lime should be applied to the field.

In 1912, Truog, who had just received his M.A. in science, had a Chinese graduate student working under him and they decided to investigate methods for testing soil acidity. This was a particularly pertinent problem in Wisconsin where more than half the soil was actually acid. Some of it was so acid that clover and alfalfa would not grow on it, and farmers were slow to learn to use scientific methods of combating this condition. Part of the problem admittedly was educational. Farmers needed to be taught to use what science had already established. But Truog was looking for a test that would make teaching more accurate—one that would determine the degree of acidity. Otherwise the farmer was in the position of a sick patient who knows a certain medicine can cure what is wrong with him but does not know whether to take a drop, a teaspoonful, or to drain the bottle.

Truog's chemistry had taught him that many common acids will drive hydrogen sulphide gas from zinc sulphide. He conceived the idea of detecting acidity in soil by using the soil itself as a possible source of acid, or acids, that would drive this smelly gas out of zinc sulphide. To accomplish this, he would mix soil with water, add zinc sulphide, boil the mixture and let his nose tell him if hydrogen sulphide was escaping. Further experimenting taught him that by adding another substance to his mixture, he could not only release the hydrogen sulphide gas but release it in such a way that it was measurable. Measurement was what farmers needed to tell them how much or how little lime would cure their soil's sickness.

To achieve measurement, Truog simply placed a sheet of lead acetate paper over the mouth of the flask containing the boiling mixture. By comparing the discoloration occurring after a specified period with a standard color chart, the degree of acidity and the amount of lime needed by the soil were revealed. This was the first accurate soil test devised that could be made in the field. It marked the beginning of "quick" soil tests which later came into extensive use. County agents could demonstrate it either in or out of doors, and it became widely used all over the United States and in some foreign countries. It is no longer extensively used because the invention of a new color indicator made it possible to detect and measure accurately both acidity and alkalinity in terms of the now universally adopted pH scale. This can be done quickly without the use of fire.

With the use of these new indicators, Truog in the 1930's devised his simpler Truog Soil Reaction Tester. It consists mainly of a small porcelain plate with four cavities for soil samples, a spatula, a bottle of special indicator fluid, a bottle of white powder and a standard color chart, all in a pocket-size case. In a few minutes this Tester gives an accurate picture of soil acidity and alkalinity and a gauge for the amount of lime needed. In its simplest form this outfit was inexpensive enough for any farmer to use and it is still widely used today, providing, as it does, the most accurate of the

simple tests. Later Truog devised his Combination Soil
Tester which, besides giving soil reaction, determines the
amounts of the seven principal plant nutrients available in
soil. This, too, comes in a handy carrying case and can be
used without special training in chemistry. It is sold abroad
as well as in America.

One of the problems to catch this soil scientist's attention
had to do with various methods of applying fertilizers. At
that time it was believed fertilizers should practically always
be broadcast over the land. Some agriculturists were beginning to doubt if this were so, and Professor Truog headed
a national committee which started experiments in many
sections of the country, using various soils, crops and fertilizers. The results showed that methods of applying fertilizers locally—that is, near the plant or seed rather than
broadcast over the field—is often more effective as well as
more economical. Today, most of the fertilizer, especially for
row crops like corn and potatoes, is placed in the row near
the seed or young plant. The adoption of this method is a
prime factor in the unusually large yields of many crops
today.

The deeper Emil Truog got into his investigations of soils
the more boundless and fascinating they proved to be. This
was especially true as scientists in other fields kept discovering one element after another in the composition of the
human body that had not been known to be there earlier.
Since the human body rebuilds itself completely a number of
times in an ordinary lifetime, Professor Truog knew how
necessary it was that soils supply the plants that produce the
foods eaten by human beings not only with calcium, phosphorus, iron and several other elements as had once been

thought necessary, but with all these other mineral elements now known to be essential for building new blood, bone, muscle and tissue. He knew that nature provides body-building elements in soils and plants first, and that both man and beast must depend upon food grown in good soil in order to supply the body with all of the rebuilding material it needs every day of its life.

Back on his father's livestock farm he had learned how greatly animals were affected by soil conditions. Now he was seeing these effects in exaggerated form through the work of the Agricultural Experiment Station with which the University's College of Agriculture was in close contact. Cows would be brought in, scrawny and emaciated as a result of having been fed on a ration grown in phosphorus-depleted soils. They would be fed a ration high in phosphorus, and in the course of several months would be sleek and healthy and producing half again as much milk. If animals suffered from food grown on minerally depleted soils, might human beings not be handicapped for the same reason?

As a soil scientist Truog saw this problem from two angles. Obviously soils needed to be replenished with minerals when they became depleted of them. Just as obviously, though not so easy to do, each soil needed to be kept in proper condition for giving up its mineral elements generously to the food plants that grew in it. A soil can contain sources of mineral elements and yet not be in condition to pass these elements from their source to plants. A whole new type of chemical science had to be evolved in order to learn how to nurture soils properly so they may fulfill their function in growing food for man. This was a science scarcely dreamed of when Emil Truog had been a boy.

The new group of soil scientists, of whom he became one, were men who realized that basic soil health could be achieved only by careful investigation and study of nature's laws and learning how to work with—not against—them. They had to do some of their work in the face of commercial groups who could promise farmers quick results with new types of more or less quack fertilizers which were of little or no use. The chemicals in some of these fertilizers acted much as do drugs which, administered when a man is in a depleted state of health and energy, overstimulate him to efforts that enable him to overspend himself till he either drops dead or succumbs to a long period of illness.

The genuine soil scientist looks at scanty harvests, and at destructive pests and blights which attack plants, much as a physician regards loss of energy, headaches and visible outer symptoms in a human being. They are nature's signposts saying, "Something is wrong. Worse trouble ahead." They challenge soil scientist and physician alike to seek their inner cause, and find how to remove the cause responsible for the symptoms. Scientist Truog and others who set to work upon acid soil problems eventually learned that the acids which produced the illness were actually the very backbone of good soil! To try to eliminate the acids is to try to kill the life in the soil. They are a granary in which all kinds of mineral elements are stored for easy withdrawal by growing plants, but these precious acids need a constant supply of bases in order to keep the withdrawal process in action. Thus, an acid soil condition creates symptoms the farmer can see, as easily as a physician sees a rash on a child's face, which tell him that the supply of bases is running low.

This explains why some types of fertilizers, when used

alone, have helped speed the depletion of millions of America's food-growing acres. They are able to stimulate, for a short period, the growth of plants which withdraw other mineral elements from the soil without replenishing it with the elements found in the right kind of fertilizers, such as lime or wood ashes. The result is exactly what happens when money in a bank deposit is treated in this way. Unless proper new deposits are made, eventually no money is left to be withdrawn.

Emil Truog's main contributions to soil science have been in solving some of the problems of our plant-nutrient-depleted soils. As he was making them, he was carrying his full share of teaching at the University of Wisconsin's College of Agriculture and of work at its Agricultural Experiment Station. He had a particular interest in the State Soils Laboratories which, after making soil analyses for Wisconsin farmers, gave them recommendations for the scientific use of fertilizers. University and both state and federal governments co-operated in this, helping the state's farmers to rehabilitate soils which, like those on his father's farm, had begun to yield scanty harvests after comparatively brief periods of improper agricultural methods. Moreover, despite his heavy load at the University, he fulfilled his boyhood dream of being a good farmer. He restored the Truog farm to even greater productivity than existed on it shortly after his father had grubbed and cleared it and learned how to maintain its productivity. So he may justly be called a good farmer as well as a good soil scientist.

Quite possibly the work he has done which will accomplish the greatest results in the long run is his teaching. He was not satisfied merely to maintain a good undergraduate curricu-

lum at the University, but he developed a post graduate
curriculum in the Department of Soils which attracted students from countries as far away as China and Australia.
Before his retirement at the age of seventy, scores of these
foreign-born students had received doctorates in soil science
under his supervision. At one stage of his teaching career it
was said that more students had taken doctorates under his
direction than under any other professor at the University
of Wisconsin.

Professor Truog had passed his seventy-fifth birthday when
he was able to greet some of those students during the
Seventh International Congress of the International Society
of Soil Science which was held on his University's campus in
the summer of 1960. As manager of that congress and chair-
man of its finance committee which had raised over $100,000
in cash to make the congress possible, he had the satisfaction
of seeing soil scientists from more than sixty countries join
delegates from the United States and Canada—some 1400
in all—in Madison for this interchange of agriculturally valuable knowledge and the furthering of personal relationships
which are in line with the Society's aim of alleviating hunger
and promoting peace. For Professor Truog, this was one of
the biggest jobs he had ever undertaken, and he carried it
off as successfully as a man half his age could have done.

Of all the fields of science open to young people in the
latter half of the twentieth century, none is of greater importance to the achievement of a lasting world peace than soil
science. Without its development the world's growing population cannot exist in health. Young though our country is
in comparison with the rest of the world, no American need
travel far from his own door to see the barren fields which

demonstrate how quickly our forefathers exhausted the fertility of soils, often—as was true of Professor Truog's father—without knowing how to avoid it. Because of a few men, among whom none stands out more preeminently than Emil Truog, ignorance is no longer the valid excuse for impoverished soil that it once was. A great work lies ahead in this realm for our young people if the foundation essential for world peace is to be created.

VLADIMIR K. ZWORYKIN

(1889–   )

Expert in the Field of Electronics and Its Application to Television and Electron Microscopy

◆

SCIENCE AND TECHNOLOGY have a universal language all their own. Vladimir Zworykin, watching wheels turn in rutted roads, seeing the pendulum of a clock swing back and forth in his father's home in Russia, and eventually gazing upon his first airplane and electric light, was fascinated by the same mechanical mysteries that were fascinating American boys in the early 1900's. True, he was thinking and talking about these mysteries in Russian words. But beyond and beneath the words was the identical idea. Whether a boy asks what makes those wheels go round in English, Russian, or Abyssinian, his mind has gone beyond words into the realm of the universal idea beneath them.

Zworykin became one of America's—and that means one of the world's—foremost authorities on television. Furthermore, the electron microscope, which first became available for operation by competent laboratory workers in America in 1941 and immediately offered to the medical world the opportunity to magnify a germ or other tiny object 100,000 times, was developed under Zworykin's supervision and with his active help. American life is richer today because this young man, born in Russia in 1889, came to America and was given a place in American industrial laboratories where he could express himself in the silent speech of science and technology before he had mastered the new language with which he had to communicate with his fellow workers.

Vladimir's parents were wise in not trying to force their children to fit into lives they would have chosen for them. His father, a prominent industrialist of Mourom and interested in banking, shipping, and other commerce, naturally hoped his son would want to come into the business with him. But when the boy showed an early interest in scientific subjects, when he preferred to remain in school after hours to help his teachers in the high-school laboratory for the reward of learning from them and also being able to carry on a few experiments of his own, his parents put nothing in his way. Instead, they approved his choice and, following his graduation from high school, sent him to the Institute of Technology at St. Petersburg.

In the Institute at that time was a professor of physics, Boris Rosing, who was already looking ahead to the solution of practical television through the development of a cathode-ray receiving set. (A cathode-ray tube is a vacuum tube containing the screen on which a picture is reproduced in the receiver.) So it happened that young Zworykin became interested in the problems of television before he became interested in radio—a process which was the exact reverse of the experience of most American boys of that day. The contact between the student, Zworykin, and the teacher, Rosing, created another of those memorable relationships in which a younger man was inspired with a vision for a life-work. Professor Rosing selected this one of all his students to assist him in his private laboratory and was in no small measure responsible for the young man's profound interest in the application of electronics to the problems of television.

Zworykin's next step was to go to Paris so that he might continue his studies under Professor Paul Langevin at the Collège de France. For two years X-ray research held his first attention. Then, while he was home in Russia for the summer vacation of 1914, his country was plunged into World War I, and the young scientist found himself in the signal corps of the Russian army. In that period he had his first introduction to radio. The war gave great impetus to radio development in all the warring nations, and Zworykin increased his knowledge as far as he was able while in the Russian army.

The turbulence in Russia following the revolution of 1917 resulted, eventually, in his flight to the United States. He landed in New York in 1919 without much knowledge of the English language or any idea about where he could find work or even how he could keep himself fed. A difficult period of ten months elapsed before he found a position with Westinghouse in their Research Laboratories. He left them at the end of a year to establish a laboratory for an oil-developing company to investigate the cracking of gasoline by electrical methods. Some eighteen months later he returned to Westinghouse with a better position which enabled him to devote more time to working out concepts of his own in the field of electronics.

He went back, now, to ideas he had had when he was working with Dr. Rosing in St. Petersburg—ideas on the application of cathode-ray tubes for television. Westinghouse became enough interested in what he wanted to do to appropriate the money which enabled him to go ahead. In 1923 he filed his first patent applications on a modern television tube, the apparatus which was to be developed later into his iconoscope, an important part of television equipment today. By 1924 he had actually developed a competent television system which, though crude as compared with what it became later, established itself as a working idea. During this period he had become an American citizen and was studying at the University of Pittsburgh for his doctor's degree in physics which he received in 1926.

Zworykin's iconoscope (icon means image or likeness in Greek) is the pick-up "eye" of television apparatus and was the first device to incorporate the principle of signal storage which is essential to practical television. It is a sensitive device whose idea is more understandable to a layman, possibly, if he compares it with the principle used in the telephone. With the telephone, words spoken into a mouthpiece in California set up vibrations that can be conducted over wires to a receiver in New York which retranslates the vibrations back into the original word sounds that created them. With television, vacuum tubes make a different form of wave transmission and reception possible. To explain:

Within the vacuum tube called the iconoscope is a light-sensitive plate rather than one that is sound-sensitive as the telephone mouthpiece uses. This plate (or mosaic) is made up of infinitesimal light-sensitive globules, each insulated from each other, and each a tiny photoelectric cell. When a scene is being broadcast, the light from the television lens sets up faint electric currents on this plate which vary according to the intensity of the light. As the light strikes the tiny globules, they become electrically charged.

Once these tiny globules are electrically charged they remain so until the charge is removed by a process called "scanning." This is done by an electron beam shot from an electron gun which is part of the iconoscope. This electron beam moves back and forth across the charged plate with great speed, releasing the electrical charges in much the same way most children have learned to release charges on the surface of a piece of glass by touching it with a finger after rubbing it hard to create electricity through friction. For reasons that baffle the layman, the electron beam moves at a rate of two miles per second when going from left to right, but at the rate of twenty miles per second when going from right to left. The charges it releases in its rapid scanning (or reading) process are amplified and then transmitted by wire to the transmitting station, where they are emitted into space in exactly the same way sound broadcasting is emitted from the radio broadcasting station. As soon as the charges have been released from the mosaic, the light from the television lens sets up its faint electric currents again, making the process continuous.

At this point, another of Zworykin's inventions, the kinescope, enables a person far away from the iconoscope to see the scene it is telecasting. The kinescope is a special cathode-ray tube in television receiving apparatus. This receiver picks up the electrical vibrations sent out from the transmitting station, boosts them to a higher intensity and uses them to control the intensity of the cathode-ray beam from the electron gun in the kinescope. This beam scans a fluorescent screen which converts the electrical energy in the beam into light, thus re-forming a visible image of the scene picked up by the iconoscope.

In 1929, in the midst of his work on television, Dr. Zworykin moved from Westinghouse in Pittsburgh to the RCA Research Laboratory in Camden, New Jersey. With this change his career begins to illustrate some of the difficulties involved in the wise handling of patents in our present-day industrial system, especially when the need for great sums of money is involved, as it is in researches dependent upon heavily financed laboratories with expensive equipment. Dr. Zworykin already had scores of patents issued in his name. Obviously those which had been financed by Westinghouse were controlled by that company. Obviously, too, when he went to another laboratory to continue his own line of work with RCA financing, the new company would control his later patents. Yet his later work would be, in some aspects, a continuation of his earlier work and involve ideas patented in earlier inventions.

To complicate matters even more, ideas often strike like forked lightning, hitting a number of scientific heads at the same moment. Groups and individuals are often working on the same problem simultaneously in various laboratories. So it is evident how confused the claims to priority in patents may, in all good faith, become. Despite the best efforts of industrial organizations to cross-license each other so that progress may not be impeded, the whole problem of the wise handling of patents is full of headaches which the true man of science is glad to leave to others while he pursues the particular kind of truth for which he seems created.

After his move to RCA Dr. Zworykin's pursuits remained, for the most part, in the general field of electron optics, of which television itself is but one segment. One of his researches led to active investigation of the electron multiplier which can be used in a cathode-ray tube when it is desirable to intensify a small electron current. In general, it can be used to amplify much smaller electron streams than can be successfully amplified with an ordinary vacuum tube. The electron multiplier is based on the fact that when certain sensitized surfaces are bombarded with a stream of electrons they become emitters of secondary electrons. If these, in turn, are directed against a second sensitized surface, it, too, becomes an emitter, producing another supply of secondary electrons which are in turn increased by being shot against the next sensitized surface—and so on. Thus, in Dr. Zworykin's iconoscope the electron beam used in scanning can be amplified many times through an electron multiplier operated by an ordinary electric direct current.

His interest in electron optics led him directly into another related problem—that of building a practical electron microscope. Even the layman can understand the possibilities opened up in microscopy with the development of electron-shooting apparatus. With any microscope, the smallness of the object we can see depends upon the wave length of light used to do the seeing. With ordinary microscopes using visible light, we can see objects with a diameter of about half the wave length of the shortest visible light ray, but nothing smaller. The ultraviolet ray microscope, using wave lengths about half the length of the visible light ray, can pick up objects correspondingly smaller, just as smaller fingers can pick up smaller objects than can large fingers.

Zworykin recognized that because the wave length of electronic radiation varies according to the speed with which the electrons are made to travel, this created all kinds of possibilities for microscopy. Three hundred and seventy miles per second—the speed of an electron pushed along by a potential of only one volt—is slow going in the electronic world. Yet that light ray has a wave length of only twelve angstroms in comparison with the approximately 4000 angstrom wave length of the shortest visible light ray that is used with the ordinary microscope! He saw the dizzying possibilities of what would happen when a microscope could be built to take advantage of a million-volt potential which pushes electrons along at a rate of more than 175,000 miles per second, giving a wave length of about one-hundreth of an angstrom.

These were some of the possibilities pulling at the wave lengths of Zworykin's mind when he directed his own research and that of a group of specialists gathered from Europe, Canada and the United States into this field where German scientists were already working. Early in 1939 the group in Camden produced its first electron microscope—an instrument as big as the side of a house, requiring an electrical expert and a roomful of powerhouse equipment to run it, all for the purpose of revealing the unlimited possibilities in the field of the infinitesimally small!

That was the first one. But within a year they had an electron microscope available within the price reach of many laboratories—industrial and medical—only six and a half feet in height, small enough so that it would fit easily into an average size room, and simple enough to be operated by any competent laboratory worker after it was plugged into an ordinary electric light socket. It was from twenty to fifty times more powerful in what it could pick up than the ordinary microscope. Instead of magnifying 1500 to 2000 times, as the ordinary microscope does, this early electron microscope made possible magnifications up to 100,000 times and made visible to the human eye particles as small as thirty angstrom units—that is, one three-millionths of a millimeter.

Instead of using rays of light and glass lenses, the microscope developed by Dr. Zworykin and his co-workers in the RCA Research Laboratory used a stream of electrons propelled through a series of magnetic coils which acted like glass lenses in bringing them to a focus on the specimen on the slide. The slides were thin but tough films (often cellulose nitrate) and one of the most ingenious pieces of apparatus in the whole six and a half feet of the microscope was an air lock that enabled slides to be inserted and withdrawn within a minute's time without destroying the high vacuum essential in electron work.

By the end of another decade thousands of these microscopes were in use all over the world, with magnifications several times the original 100,000 times possible in some of them. Now germs of many kinds were revealing new information. Details never seen before were seen for the first time, while viruses and other sub-microscopic organisms became visible. Scientists, who had studied some of these sub-microscopic organisms so minutely that they had predicted their sizes and shapes, now had the satisfaction of seeing their predictions come true as they put their specimens under the electron microscope which made them visible for the first time.

The importance of the electron microscope in physical, chemical and metallurgical research has proved to be as great as in biological research. Its tremendous power has been making it possible for several decades to obtain new knowledge of immense importance in science and industry.

In 1940 RCA appointed Dr. Zworykin associate director of all research carried on in the Camden laboratories. His own work continued in electron optics, and in 1946 he became RCA's Director of Electronic Research. A year later he was made a vice-president of the organization and, after reaching his sixty-fifth birthday, was given the status of honorary vice-president as he continued his work as a consultant.

Often spoken of as the father of television or the elder statesman of electronic research, this once penniless young Russian, who came to the United States where his contribution to the world was in part made possible by the financial backing of far-sighted industrialists, has continued his work well into his seventies. Some of the highest honors of the scientific world have come to him, including the Lamme Award, the Edison Medal, the Medal of Honor of the Institute of Radio Engineers, and membership in both our National Academy of Sciences and the American Academy of Arts and Sciences. But Vladimir Zworykin speaks not of the honors but of the possibilities arising from the work that brought the honors, as his best reward for the lifelong efforts he has made to develop television from its beginnings to its present advanced state.

He confesses that the magnitude of the influence of his life-work upon society has surprised him, and that the absorption of large segments of the public in inferior television programs has been discouraging. As increasing segments began to show greater vision about the possibilities of television as a teaching device not only for students in schools but for citizens in homes, he has been encouraged to visualize the not-too-distant future more hopefully. He sees it as one in which his work will help create a sound foundation for American democracy through an informed citizenry which is an essential for the success of our chosen system of government and way of life.

ENRICO FERMI

(1901–1954)

Italian-American Nuclear Physicist, the First Man in the World to Achieve a Chain Reaction in Atomic Fission

◆

As a young boy in Rome where he had been born in 1901, Enrico Fermi and his one-year-older brother, Giulio, came to be thought of as wonder boys by the time they were in their early teens. They were designing and building electric motors which actually worked, and even drawing plans for airplane engines experts could scarcely believe were made by adolescent boys, little more than a decade after the Wright brothers made their famous first flight at Kitty Hawk. The two young Fermis were so similar in their abilities and interests that it was difficult to distinguish between their achievements or to come upon one of them without finding the other nearby.

Then, when Giulio was only fifteen, he died suddenly. Until that dreadful winter, Enrico had never been a very serious student of books. Now he turned to study as a way of filling the great blank in his life. Mathematics and physics

110

had such fascination for him that he began to study them for their own pleasure, not as school assignments. To obtain proper books was a problem, for his parents were of modest circumstances. Fortunately, an outdoor market was held every Wednesday within a reasonable distance of his home where second-hand books were available at modest prices. Enrico found what he needed and, before he had finished high school won the interest of a friend of his father's—a man of some mathematical ability—who recognized a similar ability in the boy. With the intent of teasing Enrico, he gave the boy problems he himself could not solve. The youngster solved them, and the man urged him to apply for a fellowship at the Reale Scuola Normale Superiore at Pisa where free board, lodgings and special lectures were provided for a selected group of talented students attending the University of Pisa.

Enrico passed the examinations required by the Reale Scuola Normale, and by the time he entered it that fall had been told by one of his examiners that the paper he had been required to write on vibrating strings showed him to be "exceptional." The information did not deter him from taking his full part in aspects of student life that required nothing exceptional in the way of intellectual ability. Removed from a home still filled with gloom over his brother's death, Enrico entered upon four happy years with new friends in a completely new atmosphere. Pisa was a small university city with a tradition of gay as well as serious student life dating back to the Middle Ages. Galileo had been a student here in the sixteenth century when he made his experiments on the velocities of falling bodies. Young Fermi, who needed fun as much as study at this period in his life, soon became a member of the "Anti-Neighbors Society" whose primary aim was to pester people, including its own members. He became as adept as any in placing a pan of water where it would spill on the first person opening a door or in exploding stink bombs in a classroom during a lecture.

On spring and autumn afternoons he made day-long excursions in the Apennines where, despite his short legs and stocky body, he could keep pace with students whose physical build was better designed for speed in rushing up the side of a mountain. After a day like this, the codfish which, because of food shortages after World War I, formed so great a part of the students' diet, may not have been quite as unappetizing as it had been the day before. He studied, of course, and in winter months the sixteenth century palace which was the dormitory in which he studied was as devoid of heat as the Fermi home in Rome had been. But here, in his cold, bare, cell-like room, he was provided with a *scaldino,* a handled crock with smoldering charcoals and ashes which, held in his lap, kept hands and stomach warm. In Rome he had sat on his hands and learned to turn the pages of his book with his tongue.

Before young Fermi had come to the end of his four years in Pisa, his ability in physics was so obvious that his professor in that subject asked his student to teach him some theoretical physics. Never the victim of false modesty, Fermi consented and held a course of lessons on Einstein's theory of relativity for his teacher. For his graduation thesis he wrote a paper on experimental work he had done with X rays and for his "orals" gave a dissertation on the same subject. Although he was granted his Doctorate in Physics *magna cum laude,* none of his eleven examiners shook hands with or congratulated him that day, nor did the University publish his thesis, three gestures which were customary. The twenty-one-year-old youth had displayed an erudition over the heads of his examiners, some of whom, even though the orals were held in public, yawned to show their boredom, while others arched their eyebrows in wonder.

Within a month of his return to his family in Rome, the Fascist army under the control of Mussolini took over that city. University life throughout Italy continued much as usual; and "as usual" meant that physics was at a standstill. In Swiss and German universities over the Alps to the north, Einstein had already not only evolved his theory of relativity but had received the Nobel Prize in Physics for his theoretical work on the emission of electrons. The year of Fermi's graduation (1922) Niels Bohr in Denmark was honored with the same award for his theoretical work on the structure of the atom, which he described as a small nucleus with electrons traveling in planetary orbits around it. This was the type of physics to which Fermi was most attracted, and he spent seven months on an Italian fellowship studying at a German university shortly after receiving his doctorate. Receiving no particular encouragement from his professors there, he returned to Italy, first to an instructorship in mathematics at the University of Rome and then to a somewhat similar position in Florence.

At the University of Rome was a far-sighted physicist, Professor Orso Mario Corbino, well versed in trends in modern physics, who had hopes and plans for attracting a promising group of young men to Rome who would be able to get this department of the University out of its rut and moving in the same direction as was modern physics elsewhere. Never did an older man succeed better in finding such a group of younger men as he was looking for. Within three years of Fermi's return from Germany, Professor Corbino had begun to gather, one by one, a group of young men who later made names for themselves as physicists. Among them, Enrico Fermi, recalled from his brief stay at the University of Florence to occupy the new chair of theoretical physics, became their natural leader.

One of the first things that happened to Fermi that year of his return to Rome was the renewing of his acquaintance with the daughter of an Italian naval officer, now a second-year student at the University, who later became his wife. Of Jewish birth (this fact was to have dramatic significance later in his life) she had been reared, as the Catholic-born Fermi had been, in a home that did not provide religious upbringing for its children. Like so many scientists of the present century, Fermi was pleased with his fiancée's interest in science—so pleased that he determined to teach her physics on their honeymoon in the Alps. It was his conviction that a good teacher is always successful no matter how dumb the pupil, and the new Signora Fermi, with every reason to know she had been a good pupil at the University, indulged in some happy visions of a life spent in daily co-operation in the work of a husband she had already placed high on a pedestal.

In an Alpine cottage, in sight of the inspiring Matterhorn, Enrico began his instructions. He survived the shock and she the disillusionment of discovering a great gulf between their minds in so far as capacity for mathematics was concerned. It turned out advantageously in one way, however. Laura Fermi was able to help her husband make his textbooks for younger students intelligible to less gifted minds than his. And Fermi was grateful for the income his textbooks brought to supplement the none-too-adequate salary he had from the University. She was able, later, to write the story of their life together, in which her husband, shortly before his death, helped her speak authoritatively on some interesting facts in the realm of science.

Fermi occupied the chair of theoretical physics at the University of Rome for twelve years, from 1926 to 1938. In the latter half of that period he turned to the experimental work which was to bring him the Nobel Prize when he was only thirty-seven years of age. The change from theoretical to experimental physics was due in part to the fact that one of his works in theoretical physics was not receiving the recognition to which he felt it was entitled. In addition to that, the announcement of the discovery of artificial radio-activity by Frédéric and Irène Curie Joliot in France early in 1934 gave Fermi an idea he wanted to investigate. Briefly, what the Joliots had done was to bombard atoms of alumi-num and other light-weight elements with fast moving alpha particles (alpha particles are helium nuclei and carry a posi-tive electric charge) and find that under the bombardment these elements behaved like radioactive substances—that is, they disintegrated and emitted positrons as they did so.

On elements of heavier atomic weight, the Joliots reported, the alpha particles had no effect. So what Fermi decided to do was to use neutrons, which have no electric charge at all, to see if their action would produce radioactivity, and if so, in heavier as well as lighter elements. He saw the possibility of great advantages in the use of neutrons because the fact that they carry no electric charges would, he thought, increase their chances of hitting a nucleus and with greater strength. They had their disadvantages, too, not the least of which was their scarcity. For approximately every hundred thousand alpha particles only one neutron would be available.

Like the chef who began his recipe for broiled brook trout with "first you catch the fish," Fermi had to begin his work by "catching" the neutrons. In addition, he had to learn new techniques necessary for the experimental work he was about to undertake, including how to make a Geiger counter for measuring the radioactivity he hoped to produce. These now common devices were a novelty known only to a few at that time and were not available for purchase. To buy the radium he needed to make a source of neutrons was, of course, a completely impossible expense. But the laboratory of Rome's Bureau of Health had a gram of this precious material which would be made available to him. So, in due time, apparatus and materials were ready, and Fermi and his several helpers were set to catch their fish.

Neutrons proved to be more elusive than brook trout. The scientific principle beneath Fermi's approach to them was: (1) that as radium spontaneously disintegrates, it emits the gaseous element, radon; (2) as radon disintegrates, it emits alpha particles; and (3) if these alpha particles are made to hit beryllium powder, neutrons are emitted by the beryllium. At this precise point was the time and place to catch them. But some of the techniques required for this were delicate, and working with radioactivity was not without danger.

Often it was an exasperating procedure to try to fill a tiny glass tube (containing beryllium powder) not more than half an inch long, with radon gas piped in glass tubes from the heavily protected safe in which the radium was kept, and then seal it without breakage. The bottom of the tube had to be immersed in liquid air so that the gas condensed as it entered the tube, then its other end submitted to high heat to seal it. Time and again tubes broke under one or the other of these operations, but those that were successfully sealed were hastened triumphantly to the second floor where they were used to irradiate, one by one in order of their atomic weight, all of the ninety-two elements Fermi's co-workers had been able to lay their hands on—and they had managed to get practically all of them.

More difficulties were encountered in the next stage of the work. Since measurements by the Geiger counter were effected by radiation emitted from the neutron source during irradiation of the elements, the irradiation process and the measurements had to be done in two rooms separated by the length of the building. In some elements, the period of radioactivity was of such short duration that it could not be measured after even as long as a minute; sometimes it was not even detected. The only way to achieve the knowledge the experimenters were seeking was to sprint with the irradiated substance through the corridor to the room at its far end where the Geiger counters stood. Fermi's stocky legs carried him as fast as his co-workers' longer legs could carry them. A story is told of a visiting VIP, seeking Fermi, who was directed to the second floor. He soon returned to report he could find no one above except a couple of madmen dashing through the hall holding strange looking objects in front of them.

By the time the experiments were revealing that, beginning with fluorine—No. 7 in the Table of Atomic Weights—Fermi's neutron bombardments were able to produce radioactivity in most succeeding elements, other scientists at the University of Rome became more interested in the work. Soon it was being recognized that sometimes a substance was produced under neutron bombardment which was an element whose atomic weight was very near that of the element being bombarded. For example, irradiation of iron (No. 26) produced a material which, submitted to tests, proved to be manganese (No. 25). Methodically Fermi worked up the Periodic Table to uranium, the heaviest of all elements, and found its bombardment seemed to produce more than one element. Tests to identify them were inconclusive, but the indications were that one of the substances might be a new element not existing in nature and near uranium in atomic weight. The report of this experiment, published in an Italian journal, stated that a new element with a higher atomic weight than uranium *may* have been—not *was*—produced.

In October of that same year, 1934, two young physicists making further researches in neutron bombardment in Fermi's laboratory produced a result which indicated that the degree of radio activity could be increased or diminished by factors other than the element being irradiated. In particular, when a block of paraffin was placed around the source of neutrons, the radioactivity of the bombarded element greatly increased. Fermi surveyed the factors involved in the accidental discovery and made a brilliant theoretical explanation—namely, that passing the neutrons through a substance containing a large proportion of hydrogen (as paraffin does) slowed the speed of the neutrons and increased their chances of hitting a nucleus, much as a slowly moving golf ball makes the hole oftener than one moving swiftly.

If this were true, part of the problem of neutron scarcity

would be solved. Fewer would do the work of many if those available could be made to work more effectively. It was an exciting day in the laboratory when water, placed where it would intercept the neutrons on their way to irradiate an element, proved conclusively that greater radioactivity resulted. Water, like paraffin, contains a large proportion of hydrogen. Fermi's theory was valid.

The importance of Fermi's work in nuclear science was now beyond doubt. Four years after he had first begun to catch his fish and put them to work—this was three years before he reached forty, the age after which, he had once said, no physicist accomplishes much of importance—he received the Nobel Prize in Physics for his "identification of radioactive elements" and his discovery "of nuclear reactions effected by slow neutrons."

The way in which his work was received by several groups in Europe forms one of the most interesting stories in the history of modern science. First of all, the head of his department at the University claimed publicly that Fermi and his collaborators had made a new element which does not exist in nature despite the fact that Fermi himself did not claim it. The Fascist press gave wide publicity to the "fact," playing it up as a Fascist victory in science, greatly to Fermi's discomfiture. Other European scientists were skeptical, but even at the time of the Nobel award no one had realized that, rather than producing a new element with their bombardment of uranium, the Fermi group had probably split the atom into two elements. And they had had no more intent to do so and no more recognition that it had been split, than had Otto Hahn (the German chemist who later received a Nobel Prize in Physics for accomplishing this very thing) and Lize Meitner, a theoretical physicist, when they decided to repeat the Fermi experiment on uranium with slow neutron bombardment.

The experiments in Berlin, undertaken for the purpose of identifying exactly the element, or elements, the group in Italy had actually produced, literally shook the world. They resulted in the discovery of atomic fission, though Hahn himself recognized the fact no more than had Fermi. As a chemist, though, he accepted chemical evidence of what he found and stated as a definite fact that barium was one of the products of uranium disintegration. The physicist with whom he had worked so long, however, was no longer in Berlin when this fact became clear to him. Lize Meitner had had to flee Hitler's anti-Semitic decrees so she did not know about it until, some months later in a comparatively safe spot outside Germany, she read in a British journal Hahn's report on their work. In it he disclosed that completed chemical analyses showed barium was one of the substances resulting from their bombardment of uranium. And the fact puzzled him, he wrote, because it was contrary to any other phenomenon observed in nuclear physics.

As she read, Meitner's comprehension of Niels Bohr's theory of the structure of the atom enabled her to grasp the meaning that had eluded Hahn. The appearance of barium indicated the great possibility that *the nucleus of the uranium atom had been split!* Her physicist nephew in Denmark, with whom she immediately communicated, set promptly to work to prove her theory by laboratory experiment, but not before they had arranged for the news to be relayed to American scientists as quickly as possible along with Meitner's calculations (later proved to be correct) of the awesome amount of energy released in "atomic fission," a term she was the first to use. This discovery, made in a Germany which, under Hitler, had already begun to gobble up smaller countries on its borders, could become of tragic importance.

Enrico Fermi and his family arrived in America at approximately the same time Dr. Meitner's message was received by scientists there. Anti-Semitism had reached Italy and, fearing danger to his wife, he had taken her and their two children to Sweden for the Nobel Prize ceremonies and then brought them directly to America where he was to be in the physics department at Columbia University. With other physicists to whom Meitner's message was given, he recognized that if a controlled chain reaction of splitting atoms could be achieved, a weapon of fantastic explosive power might result. It was his theory that neutrons were emitted during uranium fission (this was quickly confirmed at several American universities) and that they might be made to produce a chain reaction. He set to work immediately to try to find conditions under which this massive release of energy might be made possible.

Not much was possible without funds and democracies move slowly. Columbia received a six-thousand-dollar grant which enabled Fermi, Leo Szilard and other physicists there to buy some materials with which to start their research. In August of that year (1939) Albert Einstein informed President Roosevelt that the Fermi-Szilard work led him "to expect that the element uranium may be turned into a new and important source of energy in the immediate future" and that bombs "might" be constructed which used it. A few weeks later Europe was at war, and Nazi scientists were known to be working with uranium. Yet not until December 6, 1941—one short day before Pearl Harbor—was decision taken in Washington to make an all-out effort in atomic energy research.

On that fateful next day Enrico Fermi automatically became an enemy alien. Yet so unquestioned was his loyalty to the country of which he became a citizen at the first possible moment (this was not until 1944) and so outstandingly qualified was he in the type of scientific work that was needed, he was called to Chicago to work on the secret project which, early the following December, achieved the first chain reaction of splitting atoms and foretold the first atomic bomb.

The atomic pile within which the chain reaction was achieved was made, as smaller piles at Columbia and Chicago had been, of layers of pure graphite bricks alternating with bricks in which chunks of uranium were embedded in the graphite. Graphite is carbon. Carbon was found to be better suited for controlling the speed of neutrons in a pile than the hydrogen in paraffin or water. Fermi's speed as well as his competence in directing the project in Chicago served America well in those critical days. He knew his neutrons! And when December 2, 1942, arrived to become a red letter date in history, it was Enrico Fermi who directed the pulling, one by one, of the cadmium rods (cadmium absorbs neutrons) from the atomic pile, removal of the last of which would permit the chain reaction to start.

"Pull it out another foot," he directed George Weil who was handling the last rod. Weil obeyed. "Now the pile will react," said Fermi with complete faith in his basic theories and ideas that had gone into its construction. And react it did! Under perfect control, atomic energy was released in a chain reaction.

That afternoon, when Arthur Compton, Director of the

Manhattan Project, telephoned his message of success to authorities elsewhere, he gave it in these words: "The Italian navigator has reached the New World."

The next job in the all-out effort in atomic energy research was to create a bomb before Hitler's scientists. Now Fermi's importance was such that a powerfully built bodyguard accompanied him everywhere. His family grew used to having him leave on trips to unknown destinations they learned later had been sites of various atomic piles where his theory and know-how of neutron behavior were needed. When an isolated spot near Santa Fe, New Mexico, was selected as the site where work on the first atomic bomb was to concentrate, Fermi was made Associate Director of the Los Alamos Laboratory and moved his family there.

The success of the Los Alamos project is too well known to need recounting here, and Fermi had a great part in its success. The citation on his Congressional Medal of Merit notes his sound scientific judgment, his initiative, resourcefulness and unswerving devotion to duty. Two of his other gifts—his power of concentration and his ability to make simple measurements without the use of outside tools—were probably never better illustrated than on the day the test bomb was exploded. Even as a boy, Fermi could place his thumb near one eye, close the other and measure with accuracy the height of a tree or the distance of a range of mountains. In July, 1945, as a man about to witness the explosion of the first atomic bomb, he stood dropping pieces of paper, watching them fall at his feet. When the blast following the explosion hit them, they were dragged some distance away. He paced the distance, measured it by counting his steps, and *calculated the power of the explosion in figures that coincided with those of precision instruments.* When asked about the noise of the explosion he admitted he had not been much aware of it, so concentrated had he been upon his own work.

Fermi's last years were spent as Professor of Physics at the University of Chicago where he continued his investigations of neutrons, adding investigations of mesons to them when the new cyclotron made meson study possible. He lived only a short time, however, after learning the new techniques necessary for meson study. Cancer felled him at the age of fifty-three. Two days before his death in 1954, he received a special award of $25,000 from the U.S. Atomic Energy Commission for his achievements. Today that Commission's award for achievement in its field bears Enrico Fermi's name, as does the Institute for Nuclear Physics at the University of Chicago.

Three years after his death something happened that would surely have pleased this great physicist had he lived to see it. Two of his graduate students, Chinese-born T.D. Lee and C.N. Yang, received the Nobel Prize in Physics. They gave tremendous credit for their work to Enrico Fermi's teaching, for the lucidity with which he helped them to distinguish what is good in physics from what is not.

PAUL ALLMAN SIPLE

(1908–   )

Explorer-Geographer-Scientist Whose Discoveries in
Antarctica and Studies of Its Climatology Brought Him
International Renown

◈

Paul siple was nineteen when he started off on his first
trip to Antarctica. He was—as judged by younger men sharing the hardships of life on that rigorous continent—"an old
man nearing fifty" when he returned to America from his
sixth trip there. He went first as the Boy Scout chosen from
among 60,000 applicants to accompany Commander Richard
E. Byrd on his first trip to the South Pole. This was the
expedition in which Byrd gave the name "Little America"
to the base he established on the Ross Ice Shelf some eight
hundred miles from the geographic South Pole, and during
which he became the first man to fly over the South Pole.
Siple's sixth trip was made as Science Leader of the U.S.
Amundsen-Scott South Pole Station during the International
Geophysical Year and as Deputy Officer in Charge of the
U.S. Antarctic Program in its entirety.

Born in Ohio in 1908, Siple had grown up in Erie, Pennsylvania, graduated from high school there and completed a year in college before he first visited the Antarctic. Between his first and sixth trips there he had received a bachelor's degree in biology, a doctorate in geography and had spent four other periods exploring and mapping Antarctica. During all of World War II he had served the U.S. Army as a specialist in combating problems arising from the effects of severe weather conditions on men in the armed services. Through it all he had established himself so highly as an authority on Antarctica that he was chosen by the president of our National Academy of Sciences to be one of the small group of scientists named to the United States National Committee for International Geophysical Year, a project in which thousands of scientists from scores of nations participated.

The Boy Scout who set out in August, 1928, to work his passage on the *City of New York* had taken on a job that tested the strength of all of the one hundred and sixty pounds in his six-foot-plus body. An eighteen-hour-a-day work schedule was in operation during the hundred days of the trip as far as New Zealand, where Commander Byrd was to join them, on a vintage 1882 ship whose billowing sails were a welcome adjunct to a steam engine with power equal to that of a modern automobile. The work was not made any easier by short water rations and spoiled meat or the maximum of five hours of unbroken sleep permitted under the long watches imposed upon the crew. Even those uninterrupted five hours seemed good after New Zealand where, along with Commander Byrd, their boat took on eighty-five sledge dogs that barked their way over the 2500 miles of water separating New Zealand from the continent of Antarctica.

Siple's main concern during this latter part of the voyage was whether he would be permitted to spend the winter with Byrd's party. Until they reached New Zealand he had had no inkling that this was still a decision in Byrd's hands. "No one knows who is going to stay on the ice," was the Commander's stern answer to his question, "but everyone who does will have a reason for it." Siple's reason revealed itself in the form of one of his Boy Scout skills. Byrd needed a member of the party to act as second in command of the expedition after they reached the site he chose for Little America, and Lawrence Gould was appointed to the post. But Gould, in addition to his work as geologist for the expedition, had promised to take home a barrel each of seal and penguin skins for the American Museum of Natural History. This messy job would be too much with the new duties Byrd assigned him. When Siple assured Gould that he could prepare the skins, Gould interceded with Byrd who eventually permitted his Boy Scout to remain as taxidermist, dog driver and naturalist for the expedition. With seven other men Siple was assigned to his home for the next fifteen months— a ten-by-ten shack, christened "The Biltmore," with an upper and lower bunk against each of its four walls. The mattresses in the four lower bunks promptly froze to the slats and remained permanently in that condition.

The dog driving which Siple was permitted to learn almost became the end of him. He had a particularly close call one day when Holly, his grey husky lead dog, went plunging off down hill toward the precipitious edge of the ice barrier beyond which was a drop into oblivion. Holly turned a deaf ear to her driver's commands; pressure of the brake had little if any effect. Only the fact that a man was near enough—and brave and quick-witted enough—to leap in among the dogs and throw them into a fighting, snarling mass kept Paul Siple a few scant feet on the favorable side of the precipice.

The penguins gave him some trouble, too, after Commander Byrd had asked him to catch some and keep them alive for taking back to zoos in the United States. They looked to him like foolish creatures as they stood around like huge bottles. But he learned from experience, when they kept escaping from the open pit which had been dug for them in the snow and ice, that they had an uncanny ingenuity. When a picket fence was put around the top of the pit, the penguins pulled the pickets out with their bills and walked off. When gasoline barrels, set on end and tied together all around the pit, made too high a barrier for an individual penguin to cope with successfully, they stood on one another's shoulders like tumbling teams and got over the top. The problem was solved only by having a human being check on them each hour and to so disrupt their progress that they had to start all over again.

The result of Paul Siple's first trip to Antarctica was the development of a Boy Scout into a man with a keen desire to return to the seventh continent as a scientist. Byrd told him on the way home, that spring of 1930, that he wanted him with him on a second expedition he planned for 1932. Siple returned to Allegheny College to see if he could accomplish his remaining three years of work in two. Here he had the good fortune of understanding and help from a man who was a great teacher as well as a competent biologist and, with co-operation from Dr. Chester A. Darling, he earned his B.S. in 1932. Meanwhile Byrd had had to postpone his second expedition until 1933. So, with only a knapsack for luggage,

Siple started off on travels of his own, financed sparingly by his book, *A Boy Scout with Byrd*. While in the Near East he met, by chance, a young American geographer who introduced him to modern geography as an academic subject. He soon recognized this was the field in which he wanted to specialize. He was traveling in Africa, early in 1933, when a message from Byrd reached him, calling him back to America.

On their second Antarctic expedition, Paul Siple was chief biologist, a job he says he was hardly qualified for professionally. But because he had the type of Antarctic experience the scientifically experienced research men on his staff lacked, Byrd selected him as the best man to serve as administrator of the department while he directed other work, too. It was during this second trip that Byrd and Siple took a walk one day and discovered that huge ice cracks were permitting the ice shelf on which they had erected their station, Little America II, to move up and down so freely it was in danger of floating off to sea with them. At a meeting of all the men that night, it was decided to move supplies for a six-month emergency to a solid ice shelf a mile and a half away and run the risk of staying where they were in the hope that the approaching winter night (April 22 to August 22) would bring temperatures that would freeze their present site solid to the shelf again—which was just what did happen.

By the middle of March Siple started off with a crew of eight men to a site more than a hundred miles south of their base to build and stock a small weather station. Here Byrd spent the long night alone, making scientific investigations despite mishaps that nearly cost him his life, while Siple lived the months of darkness with the party at Little America preparing for the scientific work that would begin when light returned to the Antarctic.

With its return, he had his first taste of exploring territory where no man had ever before set foot. Leading a party of three other men and three dog teams of nine dogs each, he traveled for three months in the area that had been named Marie Byrd Land on their first expedition. As leader, his job was to plan the route and break trail for the first dog team, which meant skiing out alone in front. From the top of Mount Grace McKinley they mapped an array of mountain peaks poking up out of the ice—a sight never seen by man before. As surveyor and navigator, Siple set his angles on the major peak each day and learned much about the angle difficulties of fifteenth and sixteenth century explorer-cartographers whose highly inaccurate maps today rate amused interest as they bring high prices as collectors' items.

When his party of four returned to Little America, Siple not only had material for the first maps of Marie Byrd Land but a collection of biological specimens of many kinds including eighty-six varieties of lichens never seen before.

Back home again, Mr. Siple knew pretty thoroughly what he wanted to do next. He married his college sweetheart and took her to New England with him while he studied for his doctorate in geography at Clark University. Here he specialized in physical studies of the earth as they affected man's activities. His chief interest was not geography per se, but the effects of geographical conditions on human beings with which he had already had considerable experience. He never forgot his spontaneous reaction one day at Little America when he was standing on a plank a few inches from the floor, driving nails, and something stung him on the lip. Unable to see clearly because the day was so dim, he struck at his lip with his mitted hand, lost his balance and fell to the floor with whatever was stinging him "pulling till I thought my lip would be torn off." Finally he discovered that the metal nut on the end of a string which he was using as a plumb bob had touched and immediately frozen to his lip. In the minus fifty to sixty degree temperature, he warmed the bob in his cupped hands, slowly bringing it to the stage where he could take it into his mouth and release it.

Not only did he have much practical experience to bring to his academic work, but Paul Siple had also developed the art of companionship in isolated groups while developing his capacities for leadership and acceptance of heavier responsibilities. So it was little wonder that, by the time he received his Ph.D., Admiral Byrd had told him he wanted him to take charge of all logistics and act as leader of one of the three or four bases in Little America which the first U.S. Government-supported expedition to Antarctica planned to establish there, with Admiral Byrd heading the whole project. It was harder to leave home this time, but Mrs. Siple had what it takes to make a good wife of an explorer. He started off with her blessing and eventually returned to be introduced to their first daughter.

As expedition leader on his third trip to the Pole, Dr. Siple had thirty-three men—civilians and Army, Navy and Marine Corps members—in his group, and they met with some perilous moments. Possibly the most perilous to the whole group was the time when, during the winter night, a fire broke out in their blubber house, blocking the entrance of the dog kennels to rescuers and sending smoke directly into the passages where the dogs were housed. In a raging blizzard and with the thermometer registering minus fifty degrees, they froze their own noses and cheeks as, by the light of the fire, they tried to find the roofs of the kennels buried under the snow. With sheer luck they located them and rescued the dogs, although some were already unconscious. When the fire was over, they were unable to find their way home because of the total blackness, and there would be no dawn for months! The whole group owed their lives that night to their mechanic who located an emergency generator and so gave them a spotlight by which they found their way to safety.

Had they not rescued the dogs, they would not have been able, later, to make the exploring daylight trips they were preparing for during the long night in which they were also pursuing the scientific studies of weather, glaciology, magnetism and physiology that could be made during the darkness. With the arrival of the sun, camping gear, food rations and sledges were quickly readied for cross-country land journeys, and the two planes assigned them were prepared for flights. The extent of these flights was lengthened through three fuel caches established along planned routes. In their two-engine yellow Condor, Dr. Siple, as navigator, discovered the 15,000 foot coastal mountain later named Mount Ruth Siple in honor of his wife. He was navigating the Condor a short while later when one of its engines caught fire, blew up in mid-air and burned itself to a total loss on the ground after some highly uneasy moments as they coasted for a landing.

Dr. Siple acquired new maps and charts and new knowledge gained from studies of the effects of severe cold on human beings as a result of his work during his third Antarctic expedition. By the time the spread of World War II in Europe called a halt to all their activities, the group as a whole had investigated 150,000 square miles of new territories, delineated 800 miles of coastline never before approached by a ship, found fourteen new islands, seven new mountain ranges and two large peninsulas, and collected a mass of valuable material in the polar sciences they had studied.

When their boat docked in Boston in April, 1941, it was met by a representative of the U.S. Army with the news that the Army wanted Dr. Siple's help as a cold weather expert. His work on previous expeditions had already brought him two Congressional Medals, the Heckel Science Prize and the Hatfield Award, so the Army had reason to be aware of what the services of such a man offered for its work in the Arctic. He accepted and for a few months worked as a civilian, but soon after Pearl Harbor he accepted a captain's commission in the U.S. Army.

Certainly no one was better equipped by this time to advise on the types of clothing needed by men in cold climates, the first job assigned him. Nor is it as simple as it may appear to a layman, to determine, for example, even the right types of gloves and mittens for doing work in sub-zero temperatures. Body heat loss and its best conservation are scientific problems demanding intelligent study. It was a different type of problem the Eisenhower Command put to Siple later when it asked him to investigate and suggest a solution to the trench foot that was crippling some 50,000 G.I.'s and their officers in the American forces all along the Western front that winter. Many were losing a foot—sometimes both feet and even their hands—while British soldiers were having little trouble of this kind.

The problem had many facets, and Dr. Siple's investigations uncovered the physiological facts along with the physi-

cal conditions which enabled him to suggest a solution. At
the Poles, freezing of hands or feet brought such pain that
men were quickly aware of what was happening to them. In
lesser cold, the discomfort was mild enough for soldiers to
overlook it until it was frequently too late. In the type of cold
and wet weather conditions met with that winter, American
soldiers had needed a thorough body warming, dry clothing
and foot-wear oftener than they were getting them. British
officers had been able to rotate their men in the front line
every forty-eight hours, but because the U.S. Army was ad-
vancing so much more rapidly, its officers had had to keep the
same groups in the trenches for considerably longer periods
without a break. Fortunately, the war in Europe was coming
to an end, and this problem would automatically disappear.
So Dr. Siple was sent to the Pacific to advise on how to prepare men who had been living in the tropics for months to
meet the next winter's fighting. Two atomic bombs removed
that problem, too, and Siple, now Lieutenant Colonel, returned home, having earned the Legion of Merit, a Combat
Service decoration and the Military Order of the British Em-
pire to commemorate his military services.

Actually Paul Siple was a home-loving man, eager for the
family life he had been missing. But the Army needed what
he had to offer and prevailed upon him to accept a civilian
scientist position with the Army Chief of Staff's Office of Research and Development. One of the early enterprises he established was the Army Air Force exploration of the Arctic
Basin which, at that time, had not been completely seen by
man. For many months, reconnaissance aircraft made daily
flights from Alaska to search for islands. Although they did
not find real islands, they located ice islands which later

played an important part in Arctic research. On October 6, 1946 Siple joined the first of these Air Force reconnaissance flights to fly over the North Pole. This was the first night flight over either of the earth's poles, and for it Siple and other members of the crew each received the Air Medal.

Admiral Byrd was now about to head Operation Highjump for the Navy and he considered Siple far too valuable a man to do without on a project that was to establish an air base on the ice surface of Antarctica and conduct scientific programs for training men and testing equipment under polar conditions. The result was that Dr. Siple sailed for the Antarctic again in December of that same year—1946—as Byrd's Scientific and Polar Adviser as well as Senior War Department Observer, heading a group of sixteen observers. This fourth polar trip, intended as an exploratory phase for a longer Operation Highjump II that was never made, was a short one. They were back home in four months. But Dr. Siple had added to his long list of achievements the discoveries of several new ice-free areas in Marie Byrd Land and was able to make corrections on some of the calculations he had made and used in his earlier aerial mapping of parts of that area.

Though Highjump II did not materialize, a much greater project was beginning to be discussed. Throughout the world, geophysicists were talking about holding an International Geophysical Year (IGY) in which, eventually, some 10,000 scientists from sixty-seven nations manned 2,000 stations around the globe and made studies in meteorology, the aurora and airglow, glaciology, ionospheric physics, seismology, cosmic rays, gravity, geomagnetism and other physical phenomena. As noted earlier, Dr. Siple was one of the small group of scientists named to the U.S. National Committee for the project and, as plans took shape on an international basis, the United States agreed to build and man the station at the geographic South Pole, a spot which had been reached by land up to this time by only two explorers—Robert Scott, who never returned, and Roald Amundsen.

Because of its geographical situation this was to be a cornerstone station during the whole project. On the scientific side, it would offer opportunity for man's first information about weather conditions in the interior of a continent which comprises about one fifth of the earth's surface. Also, enveloped as it is in six months of continuous darkness each year, the region of the Pole would be the best place in Antarctica to learn whether the absence of sunlight plays a significant role in influencing radio signals. It also offered very grave dangers, not the least of which was based in the fact that men had never before lived at the temperatures to which the winter night would subject them. No wonder the project of building the station, officially designated as Task Force 43, became known as Operation Deep Freeze! Nor is it much to be wondered at that Dr. Siple was prevailed upon to accept the post of Director of Scientific Projects for Task Force 43. This job would require months of preparation at home, deciding upon and procuring all equipment essential for the work to be carried out by IGY men and, in addition, a short trip to Antarctica during the winter of 1955-1956, getting things in shape for scientists who would spend the first winter night at the South Pole Station. It was a far more difficult decision for him to make when Admiral Byrd, the Defense Department and officials of the National Academy of Sciences put strong pressure upon him to become Scientific Leader of the South Pole Station for the first group stationed there, for this meant another long period away from his family. It was also difficult to take a long leave of absence from his important post with the Army Research Office where he was serving as Director of Basic Research.

"We're worried about putting people at the Pole and trying to keep them alive," they told him. "We need your experience. If you are not satisfied at the Pole that it is safe to live there, you'll have the authority to call it off before the night sets in." Of course no one could remove the men once the darkness arrived.

So it happened that the one-time Boy Scout explorer started off on one of the most hazardous undertakings ever attempted by a group of men, one in which he believed his main job would be mainly to keep his men alive. He was not greatly encouraged when he reached the partially constructed South Pole Station some weeks ahead of his scientists and saw the way supplies were dropped by parachute (landing a plane was extremely difficult and, for long periods, impossible) to scatter over the snow and often disappear completely, never to be recovered. When they were not lost, both scientific apparatus and construction materials were sometimes smashed beyond repair and they could not be replaced before the coming of the night.

Eventually the construction group departed and only the winter-night party remained. It numbered eighteen men— eight civilian scientists with Dr. Siple as their leader and a group of one physician and seven manual labor Navy men with Navy Lieutenant Jack Tuck as their leader. It soon became evident that, instead of the careful screening essential for men on this type of mission, the Navy had sent four of its seven men, who were to perform manual labor at a 9,000 foot altitude, with physical conditions that handicapped them for the rigors of the work expected of them. One, with a long record of sacroiliac trouble, became disabled in time for a replacement to be sent before darkness came. The three others were a physical handicap to the group at times, but they were men who won the group's admiration for the way they measured up to difficulties. The night set in, and it became a matter of sink-or-swim for the whole group. They were "men in a box," in complete isolation except for radio communication, unreachable no matter what tragedy might occur from the third week in March until October or November.

To read Paul Siple's account of that winter in his *90° South* is to gain new respect for and faith in our young men's innate capacities. Despite health hazards and personality difficulties, all eighteen swam together, steadfastly refusing to sink or to let each other sink. Fortunately, keeping alive did not become as great a difficulty as many had feared it would be. The years Dr. Siple had spent studying the effect of wind on the body's rate of cooling and in developing tables to show the effect of wind chill on human beings, had brought the conclusion that if the temperature hit the minus 120° F. he anticipated, outdoor movement of the body would be practically nil. But the temperature did not hit his predicted estimate. It went slightly below 100° F. several times to become the coldest outdoor temperature ever withstood by man up to this time. But for the most part the periods of greatest cold remained in the minus 90° F. At such times, and even at warmer temperatures, outdoor activity was difficult, for its performance made every breath an audible moan and groan and, in the wind, a man's breath could freeze his eyelashes together and temporarily blind him.

Some of the scientific instruments had to be reached for constant checking by going out-of-doors in every type of polar weather. Often ice fogs, resulting from the freezing of steam from the camp's exhaust pipes, erased every landmark visible in the beam of flashlights. This made the danger of getting lost while performing essential outdoor duties very real. There were narrow escapes, moments when men felt as if they were walking on an ocean with each wave like every other, and when intense pain from cold fingers and toes made the best use of their minds in finding their way to safety impossible. But no tragedy beset them. There was a very sad day, though, when the radio brought news that Admiral Byrd had died back in the States.

The scientists in Dr. Siple's group consisted of four meteorologists, a glaciologist, a seismologist, a specialist in the ionosphere and one in the aurora. His own special interests were glaciology and climatology, but his first and very time-consuming function was to keep all the science programs running smoothly. One of the most interesting discoveries of the winter was the small amount (about six inches) of snowfall at the Pole, and that, although they were sitting upon an accumulation of 8,300 feet of snow and ice on top of 900 more feet of land above sea level, its cushioning effect did not deter their seismograph from recording an average of three disturbances every two days. A few were undoubtedly caused by snow tremors and slides, but most of them were confirmed in Washington as having been earth tremors recorded by other instruments over the globe.

Dr. Siple spent fifteen consecutive months on his sixth trip to Antarctica, twelve of them in the isolation of the South Pole Station. Then he returned to his post as civilian science adviser in the Research and Development Office of the Army's General Staff and to home life with his family in Arlington, Virginia. In view of the fact that the South Pole Station was one of forty IGY stations, six (plus one jointly operated with New Zealand) of them American, that wintered in Antarctica that year, the quality of his achievement is attested by the widespread recognition that came to him the first year after his return. In addition to the Department of Defense Distinguished Civilian Service Award and the Department of Army Decoration for Exceptional Civilian Service, he received four medals, all of them important in his field. One was from a British, one from a Danish and two from American geographical societies, and all were honors for which a number of men must have been considered. He has also had the honor of serving as president of the Association of American Geographers and was the American Polar Society's first president.

Dr. Siple's work has already taken him back for a seventh visit to Antarctica and the end of those trips, doubtless, has not yet been reached. Not only the Army but the State Department, too, has used his international friendships and prestige as an explorer-scientist to send him on trips that foster exchange of information and good will in foreign countries. Though his Antarctic explorations are thought of by the public mainly as exciting adventures, his standing as a scientist rests securely upon his contributions, during those adventures and on other assignments, to the science of modern geography—that science which aims to reveal what is still unknown about the earth's surface, the interrelationships of physical features, climate and natural resources as well as its plants, animals and human inhabitants.

ROBERT HUTCHINGS GODDARD

(1 8 8 2 – 1 9 4 5)

American Physicist Whose Experiments and Patents
for Rocket Apparatus Were World "Firsts" and Are Basic
to All Interplanetary Space Flight Today

◆

EVERY ROCKET that flies is a Goddard rocket.

That is a direct quotation from an authority in the field of
rocketry which has been verified more than once by other authorities. Robert Goddard's first two patents, entitled "Rocket
Apparatus" and so unique they did not need to linger long in
the U.S. Patent Office to be checked for possible infringements
upon earlier patents in the same field, were issued to him in
July, 1914. Dated scarcely more than ten years after the first
airplane flight by the Wright brothers at Kitty Hawk in 1903,
these two patents were concerned with the idea of the propulsion of vehicles in space without the use of propellers.
Within the next four years Goddard developed and flew many
solid-propellant rockets and by December, 1925, had made
and laboratory-tested the first rocket motor using liquid propellants. In March, 1926, he achieved his first outdoor flight
142

with this motor. Thus his work anticipated propulsion in airless interplanetary space where whirling propellers are useless for performing the functions they serve in the air surrounding the earth's surface.

The first two of Dr. Goddard's two hundred patents covered two apparatuses for multi-stage rockets. One apparatus was designed to use a solid fuel, the other to use liquid propellants. So soundly were they based upon the mathematical principles governing rocket flight that, basically, every rocket that flies today is a refinement and development of the Goddard rocket.

It is amazing to realize that, although the American Robert Goddard was far ahead of other scientists on both sides of the Atlantic in the problems of space flight by propulsion, German V-2 rockets and a Russian satellite, each of them based upon principles covered by Goddard's patents, preceded any military rockets emanating from America. To know that the scientists and engineers who accomplished these "firsts" in space were well versed in Goddard's work adds irony to America's laggardness in this field. German engineers who developed the V-2 rockets and later came to the United States to work on American missiles and vehicles for space travel, have openly credited Dr. Goddard as the source of their own inspiration. Not only were they familiar with his earliest work, but subsequent developments of it were eagerly sought by German scientists who received lavish funds from Hitler's government and later continued their work in Russia and the United States.

The most famous, possibly, of the German engineers who eventually became American citizens, Dr. Wernher von Braun, has said of Goddard's patents, "This man had everything." In 1960 one of our American-born authorities on rocketry, Dr. G. Edward Pendray, stated bluntly that "If his own countrymen had listened to Dr. Goddard, the United States would be far ahead of its present position in the international space race. There might, in fact, have been no race."

The true story of the man whose pioneering work brought his heirs, in 1960, a settlement from the United States Government of a million dollars for patent infringements, shows how difficult it sometimes is to judge a youth's abilities by his early scholastic achievements. It shows, too, that a mysterious "something" can speak to a young person in silence, yet with an unmistakable strength that may give direction to all the rest of his—or her—life. To begin at the beginning:

Robert Goddard was born in Worcester, Massachusetts, in October, 1882, into the ninth generation of an early American family whose several branches have produced men and women of achievement in various fields of work. His own branch had already produced men, including his father, who possessed what is often described as Yankee ingenuity with machinery and tools. During Bob's infancy his parents moved to Boston where his father acquired a half interest in a shop manufacturing knives which served as replaceable cutting edges on various types of machines in use in the late nineteenth century. Here Goddard spent his youth, an only child in a home with an invalid mother suffering from tuberculosis. As he grew into a painfully thin adolescent he himself became so sickly that his schooling was seriously impeded. At seventeen, when the family returned to Worcester, Bob had completed only his freshman year in high school. He had done it without any scholastic distinction whatsoever and with a very definite distaste for mathematics.

That fall of 1899 he was unable to return to school at all because of his health, though outdoor chores of a not too demanding nature were permissible. So it happened that, on the nineteenth day of October, he climbed a cherry tree in the backyard of the spacious old Goddard home on the outskirts of the city, saw and hatchet in hand, to prune away some dead branches. It was a colorful afternoon and he had recently been reading H. G. Wells' *War of the Worlds*—a fact he later thought might have had something to do with the unexpected experience that came to him. He described what happened that afternoon in the diary he kept as a youth in these words:

> As I looked toward the fields in the east I imagined how wonderful it would be to make some device which had even the possibility of ascending to Mars, and how it would look on a small scale if sent up from the meadow at my feet . . . It seemed to me that a weight whirling around a horizontal shaft, moving more rapidly above than below, could furnish lift by virtue of the greater centrifugal force at the top of the path. I was a different boy when I descended the tree from when I ascended, for existence at last seemed very purposive.

Though he never talked very much about the experience, for the remainder of his life Robert Goddard quietly celebrated October 19th as an important yearly anniversary in his life. As a result of what had happened to him among the branches of a cherry tree that afternoon, the thought and determination crystallized in him to "somehow make something that would go higher than anything had ever gone before." The certain—to him—knowledge that this was the purpose of his life never let go of him. He became a man dedicated to a vision thought by all but a very few people of his day to be completely impractical.

The first thing to be accomplished, he knew, was an education that included mastery of mathematics. Before he could begin this, health problems had to be overcome. Two full years passed before he was able, physically, to return to school. Then he entered Worcester's South High School as a sophomore. He took with him the decision to "shine"—to use his own word—in mathematics and physics. It was no easy task he set himself in this. Geometry came easy, but mistakes plagued him elsewhere wherever mathematics was essential. Thanks, in part, to Miss Hill who was his mathematics teacher, he finally overcame his distate for the subject and achieved the first steps toward its later mastery. In 1904 he graduated with high scholastic honors and with the distinction of being the oldest student ever to receive a diploma from South High. His commencement oration, entitled "On Taking Things for Granted," ended with the words, "The dream of yesterday is the hope of today and the reality of tomorrow."

His mother's continuing illness, necessitating constant nursing and medical care as well as other services in the home, had kept his father under heavy expense practically all his life. But Bob had a rather unusual grandmother who saw to it, now, that a scholarship and other financial help would enable him to attend the Worcester Polytechnic Institute. Here he continued brilliantly the type of educational record he had begun at South High, with Professor A. Wilmer Duff stimulating his interest in physics as Miss Hill had stimulated it in mathematics and as Professor Arthur Gordon Webster would stimulate it later in theoretical physics at Clark University. Robert Goddard always recognized his debt to good teaching!

One of the most striking facts about this frankly skinny six-footer, who never weighed more than one hundred and thirty-five until he was well past forty, was that, despite the handicaps his health had imposed upon him, he found time for many kinds of extracurricular activities both in high school and college. He was sociable and witty, with so many friends that he ended his undergraduate life as president of W.P.I.'s senior class and editor-in-chief of the yearbook. This was in addition to numerous other activities which included the tutoring of backward students in mathematics to help pay his own expenses, and without any lowering of the academic standards that kept him constantly at the top of his class.

After receiving his degree from W.P.I. where, incidentally, he began his first experimenting with small solid-fuel rockets, Goddard became an instructor at the Institute while beginning advanced study at Clark University in the same city for his doctorate. He now began to develop the idea of multiple-stage rockets which would use hydrogen and oxygen as fuels for interplanetary flight. He received his Ph.D. from Clark in 1911, stayed on for a year of further work, then went to Princeton as a research fellow to continue his experiments there. By this time he was so intent upon his multiple-stage rocket idea and upon working out the mathematics involved in its success that, after days of research on the project assigned to him, he spent long hours of the night, sometimes reaching into the dawn, working at the problem to which his life had become dedicated. In that year of overwork he not only completed the assigned project, which was not directly related to rocketry, but mastered the mathematical principles involved in sending rockets higher than anything had ever gone before.

The result was a nearly fatal disaster. By the spring of 1913 his health had reached the stage where he had to give in and consult a physician. Examinations and X rays were made. Tuberculosis was far advanced. Goddard was told he had two weeks to live.

At the end of two weeks he was still alive, though not much more than that. For a while it was touch and go. Eventually came signs of improvement. A long period of rest in bed was imperative. In time the nurse began to find papers covered with figures and symbols beneath his pillow. But he disciplined himself. He knew—and said—he could not die because he had work to do. In October of 1913 he applied for his first rocket patent and the following May for another. In the fall of 1914 he resumed part-time work on Clark University's physics faculty. By that time, two patents had been issued to him which antedate all other patents for the type of rocket apparatus which started man on his journey to the stars.

Within another year his health permitted him to begin to experiment with larger solid-fuel rockets than he had worked with earlier. Realizing he could not finance this work himself or begin the development of a liquid-propellant rocket on his own resources, he wrote a lengthy memorandum entitled "A Method of Reaching Extreme Altitudes," stating his theory of rockets, their mathematics and their possibilities, and sent it to several scientific institutions in the hope someone would be interested enough to help him finance further experiments.

Today this paper is recognized as one of the classic documents on astronautics. In 1916 it was passed over lightly by

most of the institutions to which it was sent. But not, fortunately, by all of them. An answer came from the Smithsonian
Institution, where someone had carefully checked Goddard's
mathematics, asking him how much he thought a high-alti-
tude rocket might cost. Billions of dollars were spent later by
governments seeking the answer to that problem but Goddard was modest. He thought it might cost $10,000 for him
to make his first rocket, but he asked for only half that sum.
The Smithsonian sent him his first thousand to enable him to
get to work quickly (they gave him $12,500 in all) and, when
the United States entered World War I in 1917, advised the
Army Signal Corps to get Dr. Goddard to develop rockets
that could be useful in battle.

A few days before the Armistice in 1918, several of Goddard's rockets were demonstrated before American military
experts. They were the forerunners of all modern rocketry
warfare. The authorities were much impressed. They spoke
of putting one of them into immediate production. But the
war ended and, instead, they put all the rockets away, to be
forgotten for more than twenty years. Then they brought
them out of storage and quickly developed one of them into
the bazooka of World War II.

Returning to Clark University where he was promoted
to a full professorship in the physics department, Dr. Goddard resumed his teaching and experimenting in Worcester.
Here he remained for the rest of his life, with several long
leaves of absence, mainly spent near Roswell, New Mexico,
where his rocket experiments could be pursued in surround-
ings further removed from human habitation than was possible in Massachusetts. At Clark he met the young woman,
then secretary to the University's president, who was later to

become his wife and true helpmate as long as he lived. And here he soon learned both to "take it on the chin" from newspapers and magazines with equanimity, and not to let even the derision of occasional fellow scientists distract him from what he knew he must do—make things go into the air higher than they had ever gone before.

His first lesson in the way he would be treated in newsprint came early. In 1919 the Smithsonian Institution published the Goddard paper on flight to extreme altitudes which had won their financial support in 1916. In it, after stating the mathematics basic to his multiple-stage rocket patents of 1914, he had suggested that even a modest rocket could, in theory at least, go as far as the moon. Science writers and editors pounced upon this and other statements in this now classic paper. The distinguished *The New York Times* scoffed, in its columns, at Goddard's mathematics, saying he lacked "the knowledge ladled out daily in high schools." Called a headline hunter by some and derided as the "Moon Man" by others, he tried to correct their misconceptions and found his critics unable to understand the basic principles of the science they were writing about. So he adjusted to the situation by refusing to bother with what lesser minds thought about him or his work.

By this time he had begun the very hazardous task of working with liquid fuels. He had decided to use gasoline with liquid oxygen, a tricky and dangerous combination nobody had ever attempted before. In 1926, on his aunt's farm some miles from Worcester, he successfully launched a ten-foot rocket which, in the two and a half seconds before its liquid propellants were exhausted, worked up to a speed of sixty miles an hour and came to earth 184 feet from its starting point. A bronze marker now indicates the spot from which the first liquid-propellant rocket in the world lifted itself into the atmosphere.

No public announcement was made of this test, although Goddard duly reported it to his sponsor, the Smithsonian. But three years later, when he launched from the same farm his fourth liquid-propellant rocket containing a barometer, a thermometer and a small camera in its nose, the terrific racket it made as it soared ninety feet into the air, tilted and traveled 171 feet before dropping to earth, alarmed people, who looked up, saw what looked like a burning airplane dash to earth and called the fire department. Goddard knew now that his work had reached the stage where it needed not only more money but more uninhabited space. He understood the ban which forbade further tests in Massachusetts. He was undisturbed by the headline that proclaimed, "Moon Rocket Misses Target by 238,799½ Miles." What he wanted now was the type of support—far more than the Smithsonian could afford—that would enable him to bring his dream of yesterday and confident hope of today to the reality of the tomorrow he had first glimpsed from the branches of a cherry tree when he was seventeen. The beginning of the reality was clearly at hand.

Help came in an unexpected manner. Charles Lindbergh, then at the peak of his youthful fame and already aware that the use of propellers in space had great limitations, asked authorities at the Massachusetts Institute of Technology who, in the United States, knew most about rockets. Their answer took him to the comfortable Goddard living room one day for a long conversation. The upshot was that he was influential in persuading Daniel Guggenheim, who had created the Guggenheim Fund for the Promotion of Aeronautics, to provide a generous personal two-year grant beginning in July, 1930. Clark University granted leave of absence and the Goddards moved to a site near Roswell, New Mexico.

At this point it should be explained that Dr. Goddard, unlike many scientists whose abilities lie in the field of abstract theory, had received, at W.P.I., the practical training that enabled him to "make his own hardware." He could take his place beside any mechanic working at any machine in his shop and thus could closely supervise machinists as they followed his designs for the rockets launched in Worcester. Now, in the small shop at Roswell erected for building bigger rockets, he helped his four machinists, too. By the end of 1930, the year of Daniel Guggenheim's death, he had launched one rocket that ascended for 2000 feet and reached a top speed of 500 miles per hour.

For a brief period after Mr. Guggenheim's two-year grant expired in 1932, work at Roswell ceased because funds ceased. Goddard returned to teach at Clark, with only one machinist, paid with Smithsonian funds. Those depression days were difficult. Even rich men could not lay hands on ready cash. But in 1934 Harry Guggenheim was able to pick up where his father had left off. The dramatic results of the use made of Guggenheim funds during the 1930's may be seen today, in the Museum at Roswell and at the National Air Museum in Washington, in a display of large liquid-propellant rockets and their parts. As early as 1931, Goddard had tested his first remotely controlled rocket (using electric controls one thousand feet from the launching tower) and the following year the first one controlled by a gyroscope—a method used on all rockets today.

During this decade German scientists kept in touch with Goddard's work, even to the point of personal letters asking for the type of information scientists have been accustomed to share with each other. Goddard refused to supply details of his work for two reasons. First, his work was not yet sufficiently reproducible to warrant publication; second, awareness of the rocket's potential as a weapon prevented his sharing results with those who might be enemies in the war that was surely coming.

By 1937 the Germans were working at a lavishly financed, huge, liquid-propellant rocket research center and would, by 1943, have an operational V-2 ready for use. Throughout these same years American military authorities slept on their feet on this subject. In May, 1940, Harry Guggenheim arranged a meeting of Army, Navy and Air Corps authorities at which Dr. Goddard described his work and the possibilities of long-range, liquid-propellant rockets in war. After listening closely, the Army representative said he thought the next war (already in full sweep in Europe) "will be won by trench mortars." The Air Corps and Navy authorities thought rocket motors using liquid fuel might be developed to assist heavily loaded aircraft take off on short runways.

Incredibly, Robert Goddard was now put to work on this rocket motor project, an act Dr. Pendray has described as "trying to harness Pegasus to a plow." But when the National Defense Research Committee, under prodding by one of Goddard's former graduate students who had later become a prominent engineer with the Bell Telephone Laboratories, finally turned its attention to rockets, Dr. Goddard's work became the basis for a Johnnie-come-lately, government-supported rocket development which was begun in September 1941.

Dr. Goddard lived only until 1945, when cancer cut his life short while he still had so much to offer. In spite of a career which might have been frustrating to a man with fewer inner resources, he had lived happily and much more fully than do most men. He felt himself fortunate in his early home life despite his mother's illness and his own struggle for health. His marriage at forty-two to a younger woman as unusual in her way as he was in his, was equally fortunate—and he knew it. Esther Goddard built her husband's health, made a permanent home for him in Worcester which he enjoyed and appreciated, and maintained other homes at Roswell and Annapolis in which he found the environment and domestic peace that freed his mind when it was working on knotty problems. She took upon herself business and secretarial responsibilities, shared his great interest in music, encouraged and appreciated the painting in which he found pleasure, became an expert in taking the motion pictures essential for study of his rockets in flight, and completed the two years of college work her marriage had cut short. She received her bachelor's degree from Johns Hopkins University in the later years of her husband's life when his war assignment kept him near Baltimore.

Robert Goddard was fortunate, too, in the inner gift that had enabled him to accept the experience that came to him at seventeen as meaningful. Surely this was one of the first definite marks of his genius. The veil mysteriously parts for young people at times, to give them a glimpse of the future which can make—as young Bob Goddard expressed it in his diary—"existence seem purposive." Other men than Goddard

—and women, too—have spoken of some striking experience in youth which gave direction to their lives. Many young people reject this as fanciful or too difficult to work toward. None have demonstrated more forcefully than Robert Goddard what a wealth of meaning permeates the life of the human being who heeds the flash that tells him where his future lies and dares to accept the labor without which genius dwindles.

JOHN P. HAGEN

(1908–   )

Who Helped Lay the Foundations of the New Science of Radio Astronomy before Becoming Director of Our First Earth Satellite Project

◆

Aɴʏoɴᴇ oʟᴅ ᴇɴoᴜɢʜ today to have watched television or read newspapers in March, 1958, may remember that the story of the successful launching of our first Vanguard satellite was reported as an achievement decidedly inferior to that of Russia's two earlier Sputniks and minor to that of America's first Explorer satellite which had preceded the Vanguard by about six weeks. The chances are that, even if Vanguard I had been the first instead of the fourth satellite to obtain orbit around the earth, its achievement would soon have been minimized by those whose voices are loudest in press and radio because it was so small. Lifting the 184- and 1120-pound Sputniks was so much more spectacular that the eventual superiority of the three-and-a-half pound Vanguard in furthering scientific research was and has remained largely lost upon the American people. Though its performance is surpassing

156

all expectations, its achievements are dim in our minds.

Anyone who knew the man who directed the Vanguard project would have expected solid scientific worth to outweigh the spectacular in the work he had undertaken. John P. Hagen was an astronomer and physicist whose primary interest had long and successfully lain in extending man's knowledge of space by new scientific approaches. When he was offered the choice of taking personal supervision of the Vanguard satellite project or of remaining in his position as Director of the Atmosphere and Astrophysics Division of the Naval Research Laboratory, he chose Vanguard because he knew an orbiting satellite could be a long step ahead toward greater knowledge of interplanetary space.

Even if our military and government authorities had acted upon what Robert Goddard's achievements in rocket propulsion had offered them and had succeeded in making heavy lift possible for our first American satellites, as it had been for Russia's, John Hagen would still have been more interested in developing the capacity of satellites for achieving scientific information than in spectacular achievements of heavy lift. He is more the scientist than the technologist. His primary aim was and is to reveal the still hidden aspects of the universal law upon which our galaxy exists and operates.

Largely as a result of the qualities which he and other scientists working with him possessed, Vanguard I has established a unique spot for itself in satellite history. In the first place, it attained an orbit with a perigee (or nearest approach to earth) far enough above our planet to assure a long lifetime. (The Sputniks both succumbed to the friction of the atmosphere, 100 miles above the earth, within a few months of their launching, and Explorer I's lifetime is estimated at no more than five years.) In the second place, Vanguard I contained a sun-powered radio which will continue to transmit messages to earthbound scientists probably for the lifetime of the satellite which is now estimated at a minimum of two hundred years and a maximum of five to ten times that long. Nothing comparable to this has been attained by any other satellite yet in orbit. Because of the combination of the elliptical path attained by Vanguard I and of the type and quality of the instruments it contains, its scientific value has not been unduly limited by the technological lag of American rocketry. This fact it is well to have in mind as we begin to look at the man who headed the project that sent this powerful, though pint-sized, fact-gathering instrument into the heavens from Cape Canaveral that day in March, 1958, a few months before his fiftieth birthday.

He was born of Canadian parents in Amherst, Nova Scotia, in 1908 and lived in Halifax until he had completed his junior year in high school. When the family moved to Boston the year he was fifteen, he was accepted in the senior class of the Dorchester High School and received his diploma there the following spring. The Hagens were a large family and the young people in it looked upon a high school diploma as the limit of the academic distinction to which they aspired. John alone was different. Although he was already looking forward to entering politics, and although politics in Boston did not necessitate a college degree to win voter support, John decided to enter this field by way of the Harvard Law School, provided, of course, he could find a way to do this. To become a good lawyer was his first aim.

To qualify for Harvard Law necessitated a college degree. This he decided to work for at Boston University, living at home while he did so. Unfortunately he lacked the American history courses needed for entrance there. So he took time for a year of post-graduate work at Dorchester High, then enrolled as a freshmen at B.U.

"Since Math and Physics had been my favorite subjects in high school," he explains, "and since my four years at Boston University would provide my last chance to enjoy them, I decided to take all the courses in them I could while preparing for law school."

The result at the end of those four years was a Bachelor of Arts degree with Distinction in Physics. Also, those four years had induced a state of mind so interested in what a future in either science or law and politics could offer that it was going to take only a straw in the wind to give the slight push he needed toward science.

The wind carrying the straw blew in, as it happened, from a westerly direction. John Hagen knew that, no matter what his future was to be, he would have to earn his own way toward it. As he was casting about in his mind for his next step forward, out of a clear sky came an offer from Wesleyan University in Middletown, Connecticut, of an assistantship in its Department of Physics, which would enable him to pay his own way for two years as he worked for a master's degree. Obviously some one on Boston University's science faculty had thought highly of young Hagen's ability in this field, for he himself had not applied for the position. No matter what had directed the wind in his direction, by the time he had won his M.A. at Wesleyan, the straw it carried had set him on a course in which he was turning painlessly but permanently from law to science.

One of the potent influences in his life at Wesleyan had

been its twenty-inch refractor telescope—a very fine one for its day. As the world of astronomy opened up to him, it made irresistible appeal and it was one in which his early loves, mathematics and physics, were needed. So keenly did study of the science of the heavens now interest him that, after receiving his M.A., Hagen welcomed the opportunity to stay on at Wesleyan as a research associate, a position which would give him a chance to do research and teaching and help to finance further graduate work. For two years he commuted back and forth between Middletown and New Haven for advanced courses in physics and mathematics at Yale which were not available at Wesleyan. Soon he was deep in the study of optics, that branch of physics which specializes in the study of light and for which much knowledge of higher mathematics is essential.

In these years of studying and teaching, Hagen acquired the experience that made him realize the importance of stimulating young people of both sexes to discover mathematical talents, if they possess them, earlier than ordinarily occurs in American schools. When this talent lies dormant until high school or college days, it may be too late for ensuring its best development. The reason for this is, Hagen says, that young people possess a flexibility of mind in early youth which enables them to accept and grasp the facts of mathematics without the type of questioning that comes later. "Youngsters should have an early chance at calculus—in high school, not college," he says, and he welcomes efforts that are now being made in that direction to prevent our lagging behind other countries in scientific progress.

The geographical move that took Mr. Hagen from New England to Washington, D.C., in 1935 had a very human motive back of it. He had found the young woman he wanted to marry and needed a bigger salary than Wesleyan could afford. So when the father of one of his students, a man well acquainted with Hagen's work, suggested a position at the Naval Research Laboratory which would enable him to continue work that interested him at a salary big enough to support a wife, he accepted.

He was fitted as comparatively few young men of that day were fitted for what he was now called upon to do. The NRL needed a man to help develop the new science that would later be called radar. The work called for experimentation with electromagnetic waves. These are the waves by which both radio and light travel, the former by longer wave lengths and the latter by very short ones. Mr. Hagen was asked to learn how to generate high-frequency radio waves (shorter than radio waves but not nearly as short as light waves) and help determine if and how they, too, could be put to use. This new science, therefore, lay somewhere between radio and optics, and Mr. Hagen's interest and studies in optics gave him valuable background to bring to this field of work which most physicists lacked.

The year he went to the Naval Research Laboratory, British and American scientists were experimenting with short radio waves for the detection of planes and ships. A great deal of work lay ahead before they could be used effectively as, for example, they were (as radar) used five years later during the Battle of Britain in detecting German planes. In those intervening years Mr. Hagen, in Washington, had helped to develop special microwave tubes to act as the radar transmitters and receivers. Using radar, with a beep-beep sound to the ears, electromagnetic waves were able to spot and locate approaching planes for observers trained to interpret the signals. In due time he was applying himself to the problem of learning how to determine not only the location of a plane or ship, but the direction and rate of speed at which it was traveling. This could make radar a much more important factor in both defensive and offensive action, because its information (which came through to the observer in a prolonged whistle instead of the pulsing beep-beep) enabled gunners to take accurate aim at approaching or fleeing enemy targets. Before the war had ended, Mr. Hagen and his group developed an automatic groundspeed indicator small enough to be carried in an airplane.

When the war was over he was eager to apply his increased knowledge of high-frequency electromagnetic waves to astronomy and help develop the newly emerging science of radio astronomy, a branch of astrophysics. Looking around at some of the equipment that had become surplus with the war's end, he began to suggest the use of some of it to further research in this field. He was made head of NRL's Radio Physics Research Group which, along with other projects, decided to build a radio telescope for study of the upper realms from which electromagnetic waves emanated.

Here was another scientific field in which our scientists were handicapped because in our country no more attention had been paid to the brilliant work of a young American who built the world's first radio telescope than had been paid to Robert Goddard's work when he designed, built and launched the world's first solid- and liquid-propellant rockets. In 1932 another American, Karl Jansky, twenty-seven and already ill with the incurable disease that killed him at forty-four, had heard the first whisper of radio waves from the stars and had built a new type of instrument for studying them. "Jansky's Merry-go-round," his radio telescope was nicknamed, because its big aerial (one hundred feet across and composed of many interconnected dipole antennas mounted on a turntable) could be rotated to gather in the whispers from all directions. When he discovered that radio waves from the Milky Way were breaking through the ionosphere and reaching the earth, the news made headlines here and swept over the world. In our country it stopped with the headlines. Jansky was refused funds to carry on his work and lived to see, at war's end, that scientists in Britain, Australia and Holland had forged ahead of Americans in studying radio waves from the sky.

To return to Dr. Hagen, it was not until 1950 that his group at NRL had completed their big radio telescope. When it was finished they had not the largest but the most precise radio telescope in the world, a distinction it holds to the present day. It was with this telescope that the absorption of hydrogen clouds in our galaxy was discovered.

During these same years, 1945 to 1950, Dr. Hagen had been adding to his knowledge of astronomy by any and all available means. He had attained his Ph.D. in the subject at Georgetown University and gone far beyond what could be learned in a university by applying techniques for using high-frequency wave lengths to new types of studies of the sun's atmosphere. In 1947 he headed the group of American scientists who shared with Russian scientists the distinction of making the first studies of a total eclipse of the sun with radio telescopes. Only the Americans, though, possessed the techniques that enabled them to use ultrahigh-frequency wave lengths which pierced the sun's corona as the longer wave lengths, used by the Russians, could not pierce it. With their radio telescope mounted on a boat cruising in the Atlantic Ocean, Dr. Hagen's group became the first in the world to obtain detailed information using radio waves of the sun's chromosphere—that layer of its atmosphere lying between the corona and the photosphere—as the sun's surface is called.

The success of this first radio eclipse observation, which made possible the observation of the radiation from various parts of the sun's surface with high resolution as the moon moved across the face of the sun, inspired Dr. Hagen to devote the next few years to studying several eclipses of the sun with the equipment at NRL. He headed later expeditions to favorable land locations, traveling from Attu in the north Pacific to the Sudan in Africa and to Sweden. In the course of this work he and his group developed equipment and antennas extending the range over which radio astronomy observations could be made to wave lengths shorter than one centimeter—three-eighths of an inch.

Using these very short wave lengths in the Sudan and in Sweden he showed that the chromosphere of the sun (as was earlier postulated by Giovanelli) was composed of spicules of hot gas jutting up from the surface of the sun. His contributions to knowledge of the sun's chromosphere are universally recognized as scientific achievement of a high order.

All of this served as preparation for work lying a few years ahead, though comparatively few scientists were then anticipating how soon our planet would have man-made eyes in the skies. The Office of Naval Research, alone among Government agencies, seems at that time to have been paying serious attention to the possibilities of earth satellites. One of the two projects under consideration was a joint enterprise with an Army team headed by the German V-2 scientist, Wernher von Braun, which was later called off. The other was a project at NRL for the purpose of enabling scientists to further their probings of the mysteries of our upper atmosphere by using instrument-laden satellites which would send messages back to earth.

In order to further this project, the Laboratory's work in radio astronomy and in rocketry was united in the Division of Atmosphere and Astrophysics in 1954, and Dr. Hagen was named as its head. This was his position when, as mentioned earlier, he was given the choice, late in 1955, of staying where he was or of heading the Vanguard Earth Satellite Program for the purpose of putting a satellite in orbit in 1957, as part of our country's contribution to the International Geophysical Year (IGY).

The years that followed were ones in which American scientists, with Dr. Hagen one of the important figures in the group, did brilliant work, judging by the success of our satellites in obtaining the scientific information which was their goal. Reputable authorities state that in the years since then (1957-1962) the United States far surpassed Russia in published scientific information on space. But they were also years in which America suffered stunning defeats in space firsts, made possible by Russia's vast superiority in rockets capable of heavy lift and by Soviet concentration on this aspect of space science.

Since these pages tell the story of John Hagen, a scientist who bore heavy responsibility for the scientific quality of some of the first American satellites—which had to be held to a size and weight dictated by the status of American rocketry —it is a story of scientific success. But the success of the Vanguard Project he headed was subjected to such a barrage of downgrading from our American press and radio that the American people have scarcely heard of its superior achievements in expanding man's knowledge of space.

To begin at the beginning: Vanguard scientists undertook a threefold job in developing a *system* for the newly conceived exploration of space. They had to have a rocket developed that would lift a satellite to orbit height and fire it in a path roughly parallel to the earth's surface. Next, they had to create a modest-sized sphere fitted with instruments to perform experiments chosen by the IGY committee. Third, they had to establish a series of sensitive radio receivers, running from Maryland to Chile to South Africa to Australia, which could track the satellite's orbit.

Under Dr. Hagen's leadership the project got under way, with the plan for a twenty-inch satellite by the fall of 1957. Since the science was new as well as extremely complex, snags were inevitable. But the first and third stages of the Vanguard rocket were flight-tested in early 1957 and the first test flight of the three-stage Vanguard vehicle was scheduled for December of that year. The vehicle would have in its nose cone a six-inch in diameter payload containing transmitters designed to test the capability of the Minitrack Tracking System to detect and track tiny transmitters hundreds of miles above the surface of the earth.

The launching of Sputnik I, as the Vanguard was nearing readiness for its first test, emphasized how far Russian rocketry was ahead of ours. American scientists could do nothing about that quickly or without huge sums of money not yet available to them.

Downgrading the Vanguard by armchair critics got off to a

good start when, on December 6, 1957, the test rocket exploded two feet from the launching pad. Such mishaps were inevitable no matter where rockets were being developed, but the blare of publicity screaming failure over the air waves and in print equaled the force of the explosion itself. Since such accidents were kept tightly hidden in Russia in order to increase the prestige of its scientific achievements, our press handled the occasion by doing a splendid job in presenting what had happened in a way unnecessarily destructive to the prestige of American science in the eyes of the world.

As added fuel for Vanguard's laymen-critics, a month before its public mishap, the Defense Department had given the Army permission to go ahead with a satellite Wernher von Braun claimed he could orbit with one of the Army's missiles in a couple of month's time. On January 31, 1958, he proved he was right. The eighteen-pound Explorer I, ejected from the nose cone of a four-stage Jupiter-C rocket, went successfully into orbit with a life expectancy of from three to five years. So, when Vanguard I went into orbit six weeks later, weighing scarcely more than a fifth as much as the Explorer, it was not very enthusiastically regarded by press and radio as a space achievement.

For Dr. Hagen and other scientists who had designed the satellite to gather scientific information, however, Vanguard I began to achieve more than they had dared expect. A few of its results especially valuable to scientists, garnered from messages sent in its first four years mainly through the instrumentality of its solar battery (a space "first" in storing energy absorbed when in sunlight and used during periods when the satellite is in shadow of a planet) are:

It revealed the existence of eddy currents in the earth's magnetic field; because of the exactness of its measurements, corrections have been made in maps of the Pacific and its islands which enable pinpoint accuracy, necessary for space-age travel and military operations; it revealed that the earth is somewhat pear-shaped rather than apple-shaped as had long been accepted, and that its interior is more rigid and less plastic than was thought earlier; its messages indicate long-time usefulness to meteorologists concerned with weather at the earth's surface. These and other contributions have all been made by a sphere six and four tenths inches in diameter with miniaturized instruments inside it. In addition, Explorer I's outstanding contribution—discovery of the radiation belt—was made with apparatus developed by Dr. James A. Van Allen as part of the Vanguard Project and loaned to the Explorer.

A few months after Vanguard I was in orbit, Congress created our National Aeronautics and Space Administration (NASA, rhyming with gas-a) to administer America's civilian space science and exploration projects. Vanguard scientists were one of several groups united in NASA, and Dr. Hagen was made Assistant Director of Space Flight Development as he remained chief of its Vanguard Division which put two heavier satellites, Vanguards II and III, in orbit the following year. Vanguard III, weighing fifty pounds and with a life expectancy of three or four decades, has already measured the earth's magnetic field and has sent back other valuable information.

In his post with NASA, Dr. Hagen assumed administrative duties much wider in scope than those he carried with Vanguard. All American satellites (other than a few that are Defense Department projects) are NASA's responsibility and the information they continue to send back to the earth is mounting year after year. They have given our scientists knowledge of cosmic rays, of the earth's upper atmosphere and ionosphere, and of its magnetic fields and radiation belt. Some satellites are probing the problems of microwave radio communications over thousands of miles of space, others are photographing the earth's cloud cover—a type of work of great promise for meteorologists. NASA's Project Mercury, which had launched four men in space by May, 1962, two of them for three orbits of the earth, is engaged in a long-range program which will utilize men in space vehicles for carrying on observations in space not possible by instruments alone. Another project aims at lunar shots and at eventually landing a man on the moon.

With his background as an astronomer Dr. Hagen is particularly interested in international co-operation in space science. Astronomers have always been eager to share their work and knowledge with each other. A space "first" that has received little notice in America was achieved by our Vanguard Project when it offered and received international co-operation for tracking satellites. Our Minitrack Tracking Stations were partially, sometimes completely, staffed by scientists of countries in which the stations were built. Extending international co operation has been fostered by NASA which has disclosed its scientific data freely to the world. Dr. Hagen himself headed its work in planning and directing this country's participation in the First International Conference on the Peaceful Uses of Outer Space held in 1960.

In his early fifties, Dr. Hagen is a man whose love for astronomy has helped him grow as a human being of expanding spiritual vision as he developed intellectually as a scientist. Constant looking toward the heavens, concentrating not merely on the visible sun, moon and stars but straining to stretch the human mind to grasp at the principle guiding the invisible forces of the universe, is an experience to keep an innately big man spiritually humble as it makes him bigger. John Hagen has humility. He is one of the growing group of disciplined thinkers in science who recognize the need for developing *all* human capacities to fit men for living in the space age. He does not limit human beings to physical and mental planes. "Man's urge to grow physically, mentally, and spiritually," he says, is what is compelling him "to explore upwards into Space itself." He recognizes the pitfalls inherent in the conquering of space by man's intellect and physical bravery unless it is accompanied by man's spiritual efforts "upwards into Space itself." For in our fast-changing world, he warns, "decisions can be right only if based on a strong moral and spiritual background."

John Hagen would not limit the kind of teaching that awakens young people early to their talents for mathematics and science alone. He would stimulate their spiritual awakening, too. To meet and talk with him, to read what he tells the scientific groups he constantly addresses, is to recognize that just as he was able to use shorter wave lengths to pierce the sun's corona with a radioscope, he is himself an instrument whose wave lengths pierce into the physically invisible corona surrounding the blinding Light which is the guiding Principle of the Universe.

INDEX

◆